MARCONI AND HIS
WIRELESS STATIONS IN WALES

Marconi
and his
Wireless Stations
in Wales

Hari Williams C Eng. MIEE

ISBN: 0-86381-536-7

Cover design: Smala

First published in 1999 by Gwasg Carreg Gwalch,
12 Iard yr Orsaf, Llanrwst, Wales LL26 0EH
☎ (01492) 642031
Printed and published in Wales.

Contents

Note:

1.0 mile	=	1.6 km
5.0 miles	=	8.0 km
1.0 feet	=	0.305 metres
1.0 km	=	0.62 mile
1.0 metre	=	3.28 feet
1 km	=	1000 metres

Preface

We live in an exciting age, taking much for granted. The technological revolution that has transformed telecommunications in the second half of the twentieth century makes it possible for us to communicate instantly with each other, worldwide. The immediacy offered by the telephone enables transactions to be completed quickly and, in a digital age, calls between computers are now as numerous as those between people.

A long time before the telephone became universally available and before the invention of the electric telegraph, communication over any significant distance was quite protracted and frustrating, relying on letter mail. For many centuries, the Atlantic Ocean presented a formidable obstacle to communication between Europe and America. The Pilgrim Fathers sailed from Plymouth, England, in September 1620, to seek religious freedom in the new lands of North America. Their voyage, through autumn gales, lasted for over 9 weeks. The transport of passengers and letter mail across the Atlantic Ocean, in small sailing ships, remained a slow and unpredictable service for over 200 years, until the introduction of steam ships. Samuel Cunard, a successful merchant of Halifax, Nova Scotia, won a contract from the British Government in 1839 to carry mail between Britain and the USA. He formed a company, with other shipowners, and launched a regular paddle-steamer service between Liverpool and Boston in July 1840, achieving an average crossing time of 15 days. The introduction of propeller-driven ships, a few years later, reduced the crossing time even further but by that time the letter-mail service was facing a challenge from the new technology of telecommunications.

After a number of expensive and frustrating failures, two transatlantic submarine cables were brought into use in September 1866 and these provided a reliable telegraph service between London and New York. The cables were brought ashore at Heart's Content, Trinity Bay, Newfoundland and at Valentia Island, on the west coast of Ireland. From these terminal stations, the circuits were extended to New York and London, mainly on heavy overhead lines. It has to be realised that at that time, the whole of Ireland formed part of the United Kingdom (UK) and the lines from Valentia Island to London were carried on the British Post Office (BPO) inland network. Three submarine cables carried this network across the Irish Sea. One was brought ashore in West Wales and the other two in North Wales.

As the telegraph signals travelled along the lines, they became weak and distorted and this effect was particularly troublesome over cables. To correct these unwanted effects, the signals had to be regenerated at a number of points along the route, using equipment that was located in buildings known as Relay Offices. One of the North Wales cables came ashore at Porth Abergeirch, near the Morfa Nefyn golf course, on the Llŷn Peninsula, whilst the second came ashore at Porth Trecastell, near Rhosneigr, in Anglesey. This latter beach was known for many years as Cable Bay but more recently, it has reverted to its original name. Relay Offices for these two cables were located at Nefyn and Llanfair PG, respectively.

Caernarfonshire's role in the development of transatlantic cable telegraphy was rather overshadowed in 1914, when the Marconi Company brought into service a large, high-power, long-wave, wireless-telegraph transmitting station on the lower slopes of Cefndu mountain, near Waunfawr. An associated receiving station was installed at Tywyn, on Cardigan Bay. These two stations formed the British end of a very important telegraph link between London and New York. The station at Tywyn closed in 1923, when its services were transferred to Essex, but the Waunfawr station remained in use up to 1939, by which time it had been superseded by the Marconi Company's own short-wave services.

The Marconi Company was founded on the pioneering work of Guglielmo Marconi, who arrived in London from Italy in February 1896, accompanied by boxes of rather mysterious electrical apparatus. At the time, he had failed to interest the Italian Government in his work on wireless telegraphy and had been persuaded to travel to London, where he had family connections, to demonstrate his apparatus.

The British Navy and mercantile fleets were then the largest in the world and Marconi saw a future for his discovery in marine communication. He arrived in the City of London one morning in July 1896, a young man of 22, to present himself to the Engineer in Chief of the BPO. That much-respected person was William Preece, a native of Caernarfon. Preece went out of his way to help and encourage the young Italian, and it is this period in Preece's career that justifies his inclusion in this narrative. In later years, Marconi freely acknowledged his debt to Preece, and the meeting in July 1896 was probably the most important and influential in his whole career. Regrettably, the actual date does not seem to have been recorded – life was more relaxed in those days.

Marconi's communication system removed the need for a wire connection between transmitter and receiver and, from its early days, was referred to as the wireless telegraph. As the phenomenon of radiation from the transmitting aerial became more widely understood, the word 'radio' was considered to be more appropriate. The Shorter Oxford English Dictionary refers to the use of the word 'radio' as originating in the USA, in 1915. Custom and usage in Britain, in the early 1900s, seems to have favoured 'wireless telegraphy' and 'radio telephony', with other terms, such as 'radio frequency', being used generally.

Despite the advances made in telecommunication during the early 1900s, the cost of a transatlantic telegram, whether sent by cable or by wireless, remained high. As a result, the service was restricted mainly to commercial and Government use. The bulk of the population continued to rely on the transatlantic letter-mail service, which improved steadily over the years, with an air-mail service introduced in the mid 1930s.

This account is not a detailed biography of Preece and Marconi. Rather, it is an attempt to weave their lives, and the history of Marconi's wireless stations in Wales, into a readable and informative narrative. The treatment is, in general, non-technical but some technical matters are covered in more detail in Chapter 6.

1. William Henry Preece 1834-1913

William Henry Preece, born in Caernarfon in February 1834, enjoyed a varied and distinguished career. At the age of 19, he joined the Electric Telegraph Company (ETC) in London and three years later was appointed to the post of District Superintendent in Southampton. The BPO took over the UK's private telegraphs in 1870 and ran them as a State monopoly. Preece was caught up in this change, becoming a BPO Divisional Engineer but remaining in Southampton. He was promoted to Assistant Engineer in Chief and Electrician to the Post Office in 1878 and fourteen years later reached the pinnacle of his career, as Engineer in Chief. At his own insistence, he was allowed to retain the additional title 'and Electrician'.

Soon after his promotion to Assistant Engineer in Chief, the telephone became available commercially and it was Preece's efforts and enthusiasm that persuaded a less than enthusiastic BPO administration to embrace Bell's telephone. As Engineer in Chief, he was magnanimous in his support of Guglielmo Marconi, at a crucial stage in the young Italian's career. Preece was an outstanding Victorian engineer, with an unusually wide range of interests. These embraced the sciences and arts and he was often consulted on matters outside his normal BPO duties. He was an impressive public speaker and, through his lectures, did much to educate and inform the public about new discoveries in the use of electricity, which was itself very much a novelty at the time.

Soon after his retirement from the BPO, in February 1899 at the age of sixty five, he was awarded the honour of Knight

Commander of the Bath and as Sir William Preece, he received the honorary Freedom of the Borough of Caernarfon in September of that year. The University of Wales recognised his achievements in November 1911, when an honorary degree of Doctor of Science was bestowed on him at Bangor.

William Henry's father, Richard Mathias Preece, was born in 1797 at Cowbridge, Glamorgan, where he became a schoolteacher. In his late teens, he moved to Caernarfon, to set up a school there and in 1818 he married nineteen-year old Jane Hughes. Jane Elizabeth was born a year later, the first of their twelve children, four of whom died in infancy; not an unusual occurrence in those pre-Victorian times. William Henry was born on 15 February 1834, at Bryn Helen, in Caernarfon and many years later, rather unusually, the place of his birth was inscribed on his gravestone. Richard soon became an active supporter of the Wesleyan Methodist movement in Caernarfon, preaching confidently in Welsh and English. He was also very involved in local politics, becoming a Burgess of the Borough in September 1823. By 1825, he must have turned his back on teaching, as in that year he began working at the Caernarfon Branch of the Chester and North Wales Bank. In later years, he became a Bailiff in the town, also Trustee and then Chairman of the Harbour Trust. In 1842, he was elected Mayor of Caernarfon for a term of two years. In addition to his work at the Bank, he had also operated privately as a stockbroker and had made useful business contacts in London. William, meanwhile, attended school in Caernarfon for four years, from the age of seven, in classrooms that were far from salubrious.

Political intrigue and disagreement, within the Borough, must have weakened Richard's affections for the town. He decided that his future, and that of his family, was brighter in London, where he had good contacts with a firm of stockbrokers. The family moved to a house near Regent's

Park early in 1845, and William was enrolled for the autumn term at King's College School. It was Richard's dream that his son would complete his education at King's College, London and then apply for a commission in the Army.

William moved to King's College in 1850 but by that time, Richard's business was in decline and the family moved to a smaller house off Warren Street. William was withdrawn from Kings in 1852, having not distinguished himself academically but he was popular with his contemporaries and good at sport, especially cricket. The state of Richard's financial affairs deteriorated steadily and his health suffered as a consequence. William, with the resilience of youth, seemed to be enjoying life even though he was probably short of money. He kept up a busy social life with a large circle of friends, some of whom were Welsh compatriots in London. He also attended lectures on scientific subjects at the Royal Institution and was particularly influenced by those on magnetism, presented by Faraday and Tyndall.

Josiah Latimer Clark, whose brother Edwin was Chief Engineer with the Electric Telegraph Company (ETC), was a frequent visitor at the Preece's home and later married William's sister, Margaret Helen. In January 1853, William discussed with Latimer Clark his chances of gaining employment with the ETC. Latimer introduced him to Edwin who arranged for him to be interviewed by the Company's secretary. The interview must have gone well, for William was taken on as a clerk at the Company's office in West Strand, in March. His period as a clerk was short lived, however, for in May, he was appointed as an engineering assistant.

At that time, the Company was involved in experiments on behalf of George Airy, the Astronomer Royal. He was interested in the possibility of transmitting time signals, originating at the Royal Observatory, around the country to indicate Greenwich Mean Time. For such a scheme to succeed, more had to be known about the delay experienced by telegraph signals when transmitted over long lengths of cable. During this investigation, Preece had the invaluable experience of working with Michael Faraday, and he also met William Thomson (later Lord Kelvin).

Richard's expectations of prosperity in London were shattered by serious setbacks to his financial affairs. After a long illness, he died in the spring of 1854, in his mid 50s. The following year, William and his mother moved to a house just off Regent's Park Road and Jane Elizabeth, who was unmarried, probably moved with them. Another sister, Eliza Ann, and her husband were close neighbours.

After only three years with the ETC, William was promoted to Superintendent in the Company's Southern District at Southampton. Two years later, in 1858, with the approval of the ETC directors, he accepted a nomination as Engineer to the newly-formed Channel Island Telegraph Company.

The electric telegraph was pioneered in Britain by William Cooke and Professor Charles Wheatstone, and by 1850 it had become well established, its use being particularly favoured on the railway network. The ETC was one of a number of companies that provided telegraph services for the railways and also for the public and William was soon involved in both services. The directors of the London and South Western Railway (L&SWR) decided in 1860 to set up their own telegraph network and Preece was appointed as Superintendent to organise and supervise the work. The ETC agreed to this arrangement, as the prosperity of their business depended on retaining the goodwill of the railway companies. During the course of the next ten years, Preece took out a number of patents for improvements to railway safety but the railway companies were slow to accept electrical devices, even the electric lighting of carriages.

By the mid 1800s, there was a general awareness of the

failings of the public telegraph service, as provided by the private companies. It was inefficient, unreliable and confined mainly to large towns and cities. The Government decided that an efficient national public telegraph service could only be achieved by public control and Telegraph Acts, passed by Parliament in 1868 and 1869, gave the Postmaster General (PMG) full control of the nation's public telegraph service. The BPO took over the private services in 1870 and Preece became an employee of the BPO and a public servant, remaining in Southampton as Engineer in Charge of the BPO's Southern Division. He was loath to sever his close links with the L&SWR and, in a compromise arrangement, was retained by the railway company as a Consulting Engineer. He later became a consultant to the Crown Agents for the Colonies on matters relating to telegraphs and other electrical services.

Preece became an Associate of the Institution of Civil Engineers in 1859. With the growth in the number of practising telegraph engineers, the Society of Telegraph Engineers was formed in 1871 and in 1880 it was renamed to embrace Electricians. As a result of the continuing growth and diversity in the application of electricity, and also with the new disciplines required of professional engineers, the Society of Telegraph Engineers and Electricians reorganised itself in 1888 and became the Institution of Electrical Engineers. Preece was active in all three professional bodies and had the unique honour of being elected President of each, between 1880 and 1899. In 1881, he was made a Fellow of the Royal Society (FRS).

Late in 1863, Preece married Agnes Pocock, the twenty one-year old daughter of a Southampton solicitor and their first child, Llewelyn, was born on the first of March 1866. Six other children were born during the following eight years but, sadly, Agnes died on the birth of their seventh child, Percy John, in January 1874. In his sorrow, Preece retreated to Caernarfon, leaving the children with his eldest sister,

Jane Elizabeth, who remained unmarried. On his return to London, he rented a house near his sisters on the edge of Primrose Hill, but soon realised that it was inconvenient for his work with the L&SWR and for rail access to Southampton. He then moved into a detached house, Gothic Lodge, in Wimbledon. Jane Elizabeth also made her home in Gothic Lodge, where she helped to look after her brother's seven small children.

Preece embarked on a journey in September 1875, to review telegraph practice in other European countries and in April 1877 he left on a similar mission to the USA and Canada. While in the USA, he met Alexander Graham Bell, the inventor of the telephone, and brought back with him two of Bell's improved telephones, which he demonstrated at a British Association meeting at Plymouth in September 1877. He was very enthusiastic about the telephone and recommended that the BPO should not only provide a telephone service, but also obtain the rights to manufacture Bell's telephone. The Post Office Engineer in Chief, R.S. Culley, who was not enthusiastic about the telephone, retired because of poor health in February 1878 and in the staff rearrangements that followed, Preece became Assistant Engineer in Chief and Electrician to the Post Office. In June of that year, the first telephone company was launched in London and others followed. Before long, the Government came to realise that the telephone was very much in demand and could become a threat to the BPOs telegraph service. As a result of a successful lawsuit initiated by the Attorney General against the newly-formed United Telephone Company, and heard in November 1880, the BPO was given control of the public telephone service. Preece spoke eloquently at the hearing, as a technical expert. The private companies were allowed to continue in business under licence to the BPO and subject to the payment of royalties to the PMG.

Preece was kept very busy during those turbulent times,

acting as a technical adviser and seeking to resolve problems arising from the threatened monopoly of the National Telephone Company, which had been formed from an amalgamation of a number of smaller companies. He strongly recommended that the BPO should take over the inadequate national trunk telephone network and was busily planning for such an event. He envisaged a network in which heavy copper wires would be carried on strong pole routes to all corners of the UK. He was also involved in the provision of a submarine cable across the English Channel, which carried two telephone circuits between London and Paris. This cable was brought into service on 1 April 1891. A Telegraph Act of 1892 authorised the PMG to buy the existing trunk network and to develop it as an effective national system. Preece had already prepared the ground for this major project and in June 1895, the new trunk network was officially opened by the Lord Mayor of London, who spoke to his counterparts in Belfast, Dublin, Edinburgh and Glasgow.

As far back as 1879, Preece had been asked for his advice on the lighting of the British Museum reading room. With the help of his coachman-gardener, early in 1884, he had installed an electric-light system at Gothic Lodge, power being supplied from a battery of lead-acid storage cells, which were charged during the day by means of an engine-generator set. Preece's interests in the broader use of electricity were also directed at the need to improve lighting and air quality in the major BPO telegraph offices. These large rooms, where many hundreds of telegraph staff could be present on night duty, were lit by large numbers of gas lamps, which used up oxygen and produced waste gases. As a keen exponent of the commercial use of electricity, Preece was looking forward to the day when these offices could be lit by electric light.

In November 1892, Edward Graves, the Engineer in Chief of the BPO, died suddenly and Preece was appointed as his successor, with the title 'and Electrician' added at his insistence. Over the years, he was consulted by Government Departments, Public Corporations, Railways and Electric-Light Companies. He attended committees as a technical expert and gave evidence before Parliamentary hearings. He also travelled abroad on similar missions. In addition to all this, he still managed to find time to lecture to the public.

From about 1882, Preece and others had discovered that signals carried on telegraph wires could cause interference on adjacent telephone wires. In London, telegraph circuits routed on underground cables were found to cause interference to telephone lines, which were carried at a substantial height over roof tops. Preece investigated this effect and made use of it in a simple inductive system, of limited range, that he developed to communicate between two locations, such as a station on the mainland and one on an inaccessible off-shore island, typically, a lighthouse. At each station, an insulated wire was carried in a straight line on a row of poles, the two lines being parallel to each other. Ideally, the length of each line had to be at least equal to the distance to be bridged between the two stations, a requirement that did not encourage the use of the system under normal circumstances. At first, Preece arranged the wires in the form of large vertical loops but later, he found that he could terminate the two vertical wires of each loop in buried earth plates. Pulses of current flowing in one loop, under the control of a Morse key, produced signals in a pair of headphones connected into the distant loop. This inductive system proved successful at a few localities where its limited range was not a disadvantage. In 1900, an inductive telephone speech link was set up successfully between Cemlyn and the Skerries Lighthouse, on the north coast of Anglesey, a distance of about 6km.

One morning in July 1896, Preece was visited at his office in the City of London by a young Italian, Guglielmo Marconi. He had developed a system of telegraphy, using electromagnetic waves, that promised a greater range than Preece's inductive method. Preece was quick to realise the merits of Marconi's system and soon afterwards abandoned his own. A more detailed account of the support that Preece offered to Marconi appears in Chapter 3.

Preece retired formally from the BPO in February 1899, at the age of sixty five, and soon afterwards was honoured by Queen Victoria with the Order of Knight Commander of the Bath. In September of that year, he was the principal guest at a crowded meeting in the Guildhall, Caernarfon, where the Mayor bestowed on him the honorary Freedom of the Borough. Sir William was, in fact, the very first person to be so honoured by the Borough of Caernarfon. In responding to the Mayor's greetings, and to the delight of his audience, Preece affirmed, in Welsh, that he was a Caernarfon lad (hogyn o'r dre). That evening, he was given another opportunity to reminisce about his early years, at a banquet held in his honour at the Sportsman Hotel, in Castle Street. This function was attended by the Mayor and Corporation, many distinguished guests and members of Preece's family.

Before his retirement, Preece had acquired a large house, Penrhos, on the outskirts of Caeathro, a few kilometres to the south-east of Caernarfon. His two unmarried daughters, Amy and Mary, lived there and Jane Elizabeth continued to keep house at Gothic Lodge, in Wimbledon. After his retirement, he spent more time at Penrhos, where his chauffeur had the responsibility of looking after the electric-light plant that Preece had installed there.

In 1899, Preece and a colleague, Major Philip Cardew, set up an engineering consultancy in London, and two of Preece's sons also joined the business. The consulting firm of Preece and Cardew took over Preece's commitments to the Crown Agency, while he acted as consultant to the BPO until 1904. At that time, he would have become involved in the early negotiations which led to the takeover of the National Telephone Company by the BPO, in 1912.

Preece had a busy retirement in Caernarfon. He became a Trustee of the Harbour Trust, was appointed Commissioner for Peace and was also invited to chair numerous local committees and societies. He owned one of the few motor cars in North Wales and in June 1901, his steam yacht, the *Coey*, arrived in the Menai Straits. This vessel was 12 metres in length and had been built in Barnstaple, in 1881. Earlier in 1901, the Harbour Trust decided to buy a small steamer, to be used as a working boat around the Straits and harbour. This ship, the *Seiont*, arrived in the Straits towards the end of the year. Preece sold his yacht after a few years, but continued to sail along the Menai Straits each summer on the *Seiont*, when he and his fellow Trustees inspected the navigation buoys.

At the Sportsman Hotel banquet, when he received the Freedom of the Borough, Preece had commented on the absence of electric light in Caernarfon. In May 1901, the Town Council appointed an Electricity Committee to consider the provision of electric light in the borough. Preece indicated his willingness to help and promised that, as a Freeman, he would not charge for his services.

Preece had suffered for many years from bronchitis and even before his retirement, had spent the winter months in Egypt, where the climate was kinder to his ailment. As his health deteriorated, he spent more time in Egypt and became quite an authority on the ancient history of that country. At a Pan-Celtic Congress, held in Caernarfon in 1904, he chaired a section on *Customs, Costumes and Folklore*, where he presented a short discussion paper. This included a reference to the wisdom of the Egyptians and suggested a possible link between the Welsh Druids and the priests of ancient Egypt.

The Caernarfon Electric Light Works was opened in February 1905 but Preece was in Egypt at the time and was unable to attend the celebrations. By the summer of 1913, he was in poor health, unable to move from his room at

Penrhos. He passed away on 6 November 1913, at the age of 79, and was laid to rest in Llanbeblig, Caernarfon, where his mother and four of her infants were buried.

The local newspaper, the *Caernarfon and Denbigh Herald*, in its edition published on Friday, 14 November 1913, carried a lengthy account of Preece's funeral. This took place on Tuesday, 11 November and flags were flown at half-mast on many buildings in the town. A large crowd attended, from far and near, to pay homage to a famous son of Caernarfon. The list of dignitaries was impressive, with six horse-drawn coaches forming part of the funeral cortege. The event reflected the high esteem with which Preece was regarded in local, national and international circles. A well-attended and dignified memorial service was also held at St Margaret's Church, in Westminster, London.

The wireless station at Waunfawr was in an advanced stage of construction by the summer of 1913, and Marconi was an occasional visitor to the site. It was his custom to travel by train to Caernarfon. There, he was met by his chauffeur and driven to the Royal Hotel (now the Celtic Royal), where he would stay for a number of days. His journeys to and from the wireless station would have taken him quite near to Preece's home in Caeathro and it is not unreasonable to suppose that he may have visited his old friend and mentor at some time during the summer of 1913. Regrettably, no evidence has been found to support such speculation.

Preece's surviving daughters, Amy and Mary, unveiled a bronze tablet in memory of their father in April 1953. This had been fitted into the wall of the General Post Office building in Caernarfon, on the initiative of the Borough Council and the town's Rotary Club. In the spring of 1997, with the co-operation of the owners of the house, a commemorative plaque was unveiled on a gatepost in the boundary wall of Penrhos, by the Chairperson of the

Waunfawr Community Council, Mrs Patricia Parry. The plaque had been provided and fitted on the initiative of the Community Council and the Friends of Marconi.

2. The Progress of Science

The phenomena of electricity and magnetism aroused the interest of philosophers from medieval times, but the first to record his investigations into these mysteries, in Britain, was Dr William Gilbert, physician to Queen Elizabeth I. Notable amongst scientists of the nineteenth century was Michael Faraday who, in 1831, discovered the nature of electromagnetic induction. In 1855, James Clerk-Maxwell, a mathematician, presented a paper entitled *Faraday's Lines of Force* and in subsequent years he expanded the range of his work to include a mathematical analysis of electromagnetic-wave theory. In 1873, Maxwell, by then Professor of Experimental Physics at Cambridge University, published his final treatise on electricity and magnetism. He had established the electromagnetic nature of light and predicted the existence of other types of electromagnetic waves, with properties similar to light.

The leading scientists of the day showed little enthusiasm for Maxwell's theory; it challenged too many widely accepted and cherished scientific ideas. Furthermore, his calculations were so difficult to understand that even a scientist of the stature of Lord Kelvin declined to accept them. It was not until the mid 1880s that Heinrich Hertz, Professor of Theoretical Physics at Kiel University, carried out a series of experiments that supported Maxwell's predictions. Hertz demonstrated that sudden changes in electric and magnetic fields produced electromagnetic waves in space and that these waves obeyed the laws of optics, travelling at the speed of light. He was able to generate and detect these waves using quite simple laboratory apparatus, and the expression 'Hertzian waves' became popular in those early days.

Hertz soon improved his transmitter by using an induction coil to generate high voltages, but he had to wait a few years for an effective detector of electromagnetic waves. It had been known for some time that the electrical resistance of certain loosely-packed metallic particles changed from a high to a low value when an electric spark was discharged near them. During the late 1880s, Edouard Branly, Professor of Physics at the Catholic University in Paris, investigated this phenomenon in great detail, using a small device known as a Branly tube. In this, a quantity of suitable metal filings was contained in a small space between two electrodes. Experiments confirmed that the change in resistance of the filings in the tube was caused by the electromagnetic wave that was generated by the spark.

At a meeting of the Royal Institution, held in 1894, Professor Oliver Lodge demonstrated a Branly tube that he had modified, so that it acted as a detector of electromagnetic waves. He referred to this modified tube as a coherer, because the filings became closely packed together (cohered), giving a low electrical resistance, whenever an electromagnetic wave impinged on it. When the electromagnetic wave was no longer present, the filings returned slowly, or decohered, to their normal high resistance state. It was found that this process could be accelerated by tapping the tube lightly.

It is evident that by 1894, all the components of a wireless telegraph system had been invented, but up to that time no one had brought them together to form a working system. Professor Alexander Popov, of the Electro Technical Institute of St Petersburg, came very close in 1895, when he used a coherer and an elevated wire to detect approaching thunderstorms. It is interesting to note that most of the fundamental research associated with the discovery of wireless telegraphy was done by academics, who ignored its practical and commercial possibilities. It was left to a young Italian, Guglielmo Marconi, to extend Hertz's experiments into the realms of commerce and for the benefit of mankind. Although Marconi did not invent the basic components of his early wireless system, he did discover a means of bringing them together in a way that enabled him to communicate over a distance. In subsequent years, he developed, improved and extended his system and to do so, he invented, in his own right, a number of circuit devices and specialised machines.

3. Guglielmo Marconi, 1874-1937

Guglielmo, born in Bologna on 25 April 1874, was the second son of Giuseppe Marconi, a prosperous Italian landowner, and Annie Jameson, a member of the whiskey family from Ireland. In April 1864, at the age of 21, Annie married Giuseppe, a widower of 38, and the couple settled in Giuseppe's town house in Bologna, where their first child, Alfonso, was born a year later. The Marconi family had been landowners in the Apennines for many years and were well regarded in their community. Some years earlier, when Giuseppe first moved to Bologna, his father had bought a country estate, just outside the town, so as to be near him. Giuseppe inherited this estate, the Villa Grifone, and it was there that Guglielmo was brought up. When he was about three years old, his mother took the two boys to visit her family in England and they stayed for three years. On his return to Italy, Guglielmo attended a school in Florence, where his teachers found him to be backward for his age. He was also reserved, finding it difficult to mix freely with the other boys. This aspect of his nature was to follow him throughout his adult life but at that school, Guglielmo formed a lasting friendship with an older boy, Luigi Solari, and both their careers evolved from similar interests.

Guglielmo also spent some leisure time in Livorno, the main port of central Italy, where there was a naval base and Giuseppe encouraged him to study for entry to the Naval Academy. In the meantime, Guglielmo took up dinghy sailing and became a proficient pianist but, unfortunately, he failed to qualify for the Naval Academy. At the age of 13, he entered the Technical Institute in Livorno, where he became interested in physics and electricity. The interest and enthusiasm that he applied to his studies were reflected in his experimental work but all was to no avail, he failed the entrance examination to the University of Bologna.

At Livorno, the young Marconi became fascinated with Professor Augusto Righi's work on electromagnetic radiation and he was soon immersed in Hertzian-wave research. Hertz died in January 1894 and that summer, while on holiday in the Italian Alps, Guglielmo became absorbed in an obituary to Hertz, written by Righi. This account convinced him that Hertzian waves could be used to communicate over a distance, and when he returned to the Villa Grifone, he set aside two rooms as his private laboratory.

The first task that he set himself was to repeat Hertz's experiments, using similar apparatus. As he progressed, he made use of other devices and received encouragement from Professor Righi, who was a close neighbour.

One of his early modifications was to connect a Morse key in the induction-coil primary circuit, so that he could transmit Morse signals and later, he redesigned the Branly coherer, making it more sensitive and reliable. As he improved his apparatus, he was able to transmit over greater distances and by the summer of 1895, the range had increased so much that he had to move his apparatus out into the garden. He then discovered that the range could be further increased by raising one Hertzian radiator plate above head height and resting the other on the ground, at both transmitter and receiver.

At that time, for a brief interlude, he became interested in the detection of thunderstorms, using a wire held aloft by a balloon, and this gave him the idea of an elevated aerial. He replaced one Hertzian radiator, at both the transmitter and receiver, with a metal cylinder fixed to the top of a tall pole and the others were placed in contact with the ground. He experimented with poles of different heights and with metal cylinders and cubes of various sizes. With these arrangements, he achieved yet another significant increase in range. By now, Giuseppe was paying out large sums of money for material and apparatus, in support of his son but to progress further, Marconi needed much greater financial support. Through friends, he offered his discovery to the Italian Government but the Ministry of Posts and Telegraphs in Rome declined his offer, reminding him that he should safeguard Italy's interests, should he patent his system.

After this rebuff, Marconi was advised to take his apparatus to London, the centre of a maritime nation, where his prospects could be brighter. At that time, once a ship left port, it could be out of touch with either land or other ships for weeks or even months. All sorts of misfortunes could overwhelm it and there was no effective way to summon help. Marconi was confident that his discovery could provide a means of communication at sea and save lives.

Annie made all the arrangements for the trip to London, where her nephew, Henry Jameson-Davis, was to meet them and look after their welfare. They arrived in London in February 1896 but Marconi's entry into Britain was not without its problems; he found that his wireless apparatus had been badly damaged during a Customs baggage check. Marconi's immediate tasks were to repair the apparatus and to establish his legal rights to the ownership of his wireless system. He applied for the world's first patent for wireless telegraphy on 2 June 1896, the complete specification being filed on 2 March 1897. With the apparatus repaired, he began to experiment again and his cousin Henry, who was an engineer in the City, brought some of his professional friends along to witness the experiments. One of these, Campbell Swinton, knew William Preece, Engineer in Chief to the Post Office. Swinton arranged the necessary introductions and on that morning in July 1896, at the age of

22, Marconi presented himself at Preece's office in the Central Telegraph Office (GPO West), in St Martin's le Grand. He had brought with him two large bags containing essential items of apparatus and Preece examined them all with great interest, while the younger man described his experiments.

Further demonstrations were arranged that afternoon in Preece's office, and more tests were made over the following few days in the BPO laboratories. Preece also arranged for Marconi to give his first public demonstration, before senior members of the BPO, on 27 July 1896. A Hertz transmitter was placed on the roof of the Central Telegraph Office and a simple receiver, with a Branly coherer and Morse printer, was sited some 275 metres away on the roof of the Post Office Savings Bank (GPO South), in Carter Lane, behind Queen Victoria Street. Under Marconi's guidance, BPO staff had provided parabolic reflectors of sheet copper for the two aerials and had fitted an electric-bell arrangement to the coherer. After each signal, the bell hammer automatically decohered the tube, as it tapped lightly against it. This feature enabled a higher signalling speed to be achieved.

Meanwhile, Preece was doing his best to publicise Marconi's achievements. He gave an account of the young Italian's experiments at a British Association meeting in Liverpool, in September 1896 and on 12 December, took part in a very successful lecture on wireless telegraphy at Toynbee Hall, in London. At this lecture, Marconi had fitted his apparatus into two black boxes. Preece sat at the front of the hall, with the box containing the transmitter resting on a table, whilst Marconi moved around the hall, carrying the receiver. Each time Preece operated the transmit key, a bell rang in the receiver.

This event was widely reported by the press and Marconi was hailed as the inventor of wireless. Such an assertion did not altogether endear him to the many scientists, including the eminent Kelvin and Lodge, who had made valuable contributions to the study of Hertzian waves. In addition to lecturing about Marconi's work, Preece also seconded two of his own staff, J.E. Taylor and G.S. Kemp, to assist Marconi. Kemp eventually transferred to the Marconi Company and served Marconi with absolute dedication for the rest of his working life.

Public interest in Marconi's work was further awakened by reports of a series of tests, arranged by the BPO, on Salisbury Plain. These took place between September 1896 and the following March, and were witnessed by representatives of the Army and Navy. As these tests progressed, Marconi abandoned his metal cylinders and cubes on top of poles, as he came to realise the effectiveness of elevated wires, held aloft by kites or balloons. A demonstration in March 1897, using a vertical wire aerial some fifty metres high, achieved a range of 7km. A few weeks later, Marconi and his team moved to the shores of the Bristol Channel, setting up a link between Lavernock, near Penarth, and Flatholm Island. Then, in May 1897, a transmission over a distance of 14km was achieved between Lavernock and Brean Down, near Weston-Super-Mare. This successful test confirmed the practicality of Marconi's equipment.

Also present at some of these historic tests, between March and May 1897, was a Professor Adolphus Slaby from Charlottenburg, in Germany. He was, himself, involved in Hertzian-wave research and had been invited to attend the tests by William Preece. On his return to Germany, Slaby made some significant changes to Marconi's system, thereby enabling the German Telefunken Company to circumvent Marconi's patents. With the support of the Kaiser and the German Government, this Company eventually became a serious rival to Marconi's newly-formed venture.

The enthusiasm with which Marconi developed the technical aspects of his discovery was matched by the activities of Henry Jameson-Davis in the City. He had brought together a number of investors and was ready to form a Company to exploit his cousin's patents, worldwide. In April 1897, Marconi rather stunned Preece by revealing to him that he had been offered £15,000 by Jameson and also a half-share in the proposed new Company.

Preece was loath to sever the link between the BPO and the young Italian and did his utmost to persuade the Treasury to grant funds to retain him. All his efforts were to no avail; the public purse remained tightly shut. However, on a personal level, relations between Preece and Marconi remained cordial and in June 1897, Preece lectured on Marconi's work to a crowded audience at the Royal Institution, in London.

On 20 July 1897, The Wireless Telegraph and Signal Company Limited was registered in London, with Henry Jameson-Davis as its first Managing Director and in February 1900, the name was changed to Marconi's Wireless Telegraph Company Limited. The Company acquired Marconi's patent rights and he terminated his formal association with the BPO.

During the summer of 1897, Marconi was being fêted in Italy, where the Navy had realised the importance of his discovery. As an Italian citizen, he was obliged to undertake military service and had been enrolled as a cadet in the navy and seconded to the Italian Embassy in London. In this capacity, he had been called back to Italy to demonstrate his system. He left London in late June 1897 and on 6 July, gave demonstrations of his system in the Ministry of Marine building in Rome. He then moved to the San Bartolomeo dockyards at La Spezia, where trials lasting several weeks were conducted with the warship *San Martino*. Marconi returned to London in August, and in October he set up a wireless link for the BPO between Salisbury and Bath, a distance of 54km. The fact that this distance was further than that from Dover to Boulogne was not lost on Preece, who saw the possibility of a wireless telegraph service across the

English Channel, linking London with Paris.

Through his practical demonstrations, Marconi had shown that his wireless system could operate successfully in spite of the vagaries of weather or terrain. He also found that greater ranges were possible over the sea than over land. For the next few years, the Company intended to devote its resources to the development of marine communication and missed no opportunity to publicise its product. Nevertheless, sales remained low.

By the end of 1897, a small coastal station was operating from the Needles Hotel on the Isle of Wight and in January the following year, a second station had been set up at Madeira House, Bournemouth, 23km from the Needles Hotel. Both these stations were soon carrying test messages to ships at sea and for the press, with whom Marconi had a particularly friendly and understanding relation. Some time later, Marconi and his team moved from Madeira House to the Haven Hotel, overlooking the beach in Poole. He set up a small laboratory on the ground floor and erected tall aerial masts on the foreshore. The Haven became his operational base and home-from-home for almost thirty years.

Lloyds Corporation and the Corporation of Trinity House, both respected organisations with maritime interests, were seeking reliable means of communication at sea. Lloyds invited the Marconi Company to demonstrate its system between a lighthouse on Rathlin Island, off the coast of Antrim, and a ship-reporting station at Ballycastle. Tests carried out in May 1898 proved successful, the operators quickly adapting themselves to using the apparatus. Further success was achieved later that year, when similar tests were carried out for Trinity House, between the South Foreland lighthouse and the East Goodwin lightship, in the Straits of Dover.

By now, Marconi shared Preece's vision of a wireless link across the English Channel and in September 1898, the Company sought the approval of the French government for the siting of a small, experimental wireless station on the French side of the Channel. The request was granted in March 1899 and a station was built at Wimereux, near Boulogne. Tests were carried out between this station and South Foreland, over a distance of 50km. The success of these tests aroused the interest of the French government and Marconi became heavily involved in a series of tests for the French navy. Not to be outdone, the British Admiralty invited him to demonstrate his system for the Royal Navy, during naval exercises to be held in July and August. Marconi's equipment was installed on three ships and successful tests were conducted over distances of up to 120km.

Further tests were then carried out at the Wimereux station and in late September, contact was made with the Marconi factory at Chelmsford, over a distance of 136km. Immediately after the tests, the French station was shut down and dismantled. While these tests were in progress, Marconi was in New York and he returned to the UK on the American Line ss St Paul. In mid November, when the ship was about 120km from the Isle of Wight, Marconi's equipment was used to contact the Needles station, and the ship became the very first Atlantic liner to report its arrival by wireless. Items of world news, transmitted from the Needles station by prearrangement, were received on the St Paul and printed in the form of a news sheet. This publication, named The Transatlantic Times, was sold on board for one dollar a copy, with the money collected being donated to the Seaman's Fund.

The Company received its first big order from the British Admiralty on 4 July 1900 and by early 1901, a number of coast stations were in operation around Britain, providing a wireless service to shipping. One of these stations operated from Holyhead in Anglesey. When the Beaver Line ss Lake Champlain sailed from Liverpool on 21 May 1901, she was the first British ship to be fitted with wireless facilities and she exchanged signals with the Holyhead station on both outward and return voyages. The Holyhead station closed in 1903, when a new station was opened at Seaforth, Liverpool. All the Marconi coast stations were taken over by the BPO in 1909.

Between 1897 and 1900, Marconi devoted much time and effort to a problem that accounted for the reluctance of potential customers to place orders with the Company. The simple spark transmitter radiated energy over a very wide frequency band and a receiver located within the range of two working transmitters would receive signals from both and would not be able to separate one from the other. The result would be an indecipherable jumble. Oliver Lodge had demonstrated the use of tuned circuits in a closed circuit application, in 1889, referring to the technique as syntony. Marconi developed the practical use of Lodge's idea and introduced tuned circuits into the receiving and transmitting aerial circuits. During a number of successful demonstrations, the versatility of the technique became apparent when it was found possible to work two differently-tuned transmitters on a common aerial and also, separate messages could be received simultaneously, without interference, on three differently tuned receivers connected to a single aerial.

At last, receiving stations located close to a number of transmitting stations could operate effectively, without interference. Marconi hastened to take out a patent on the use of tuned circuits and this was filed in April 1900, giving the Company a considerable advantage over its competitors. The operational gains offered by improved selectivity reassured potential customers and Company sales began to pick up.

By the early months of 1900, Marconi had collected irrefutable operational evidence that electromagnetic waves were somehow reaching far beyond the horizon. This discovery contradicted the work of Maxwell, Hertz and others. Something was causing the waves to behave in a manner that did not obey the laws of optics. A few scientists began to look for a rational explanation for this phenomenon but others, still jealous of the young Italian's success, questioned his achievements.

Marconi remained aloof from these arguments and set his sights on the challenge of bridging the Atlantic Ocean. He was convinced that with a much more powerful transmitter and a larger aerial, he could extend his working range and establish a wireless telegraph service between London and New York. The idea had been developing in his mind for some time and was to become a driving force. He managed to persuade the Company to support him, in spite of general scepticism about the likely success of such a major and expensive step into the unknown. This story is told in Chapter 4.

During their normal duties, Marconi engineering and operating staffs produced large numbers of reports, relating to wireless topics. The Company decided to publish some of these in a monthly magazine and the first issue of *The Marconigraph* appeared early in 1911. The original purpose of this publication was to inform the Company's scattered staff, including ship's wireless operators, of developments in their field. It was soon realised, however, that there was considerable interest among the general public in the broader aspects of the new technology and in 1913, the magazine's title was changed to *The Wireless World*, to reflect its wider coverage. In a cost-cutting exercise, the Marconi publications group, The Wireless Press, was sold in 1925 to Iliffe and Sons and *The Wireless World* went with it. The publishers have changed again since then and *The Wireless World* has become *Electronics World*.

On 16 March 1905, Marconi married Beatrice O'Brien, the daughter of Baron Inchiquin, an Irish peer. Their first child, a girl, died before the christening could be arranged but three more children followed. A daughter, Degna, was born in

September 1908, then a son, Giulio, in May 1910. Another daughter, Gioia, was born in April 1916. The marriage was not a happy one; it did not help that it always seemed to be overshadowed by Marconi's unswerving dedication to his work. By this time, despite his reserved nature, Marconi was mixing freely with Royalty and Heads of Government. He was invested with many honours and decorations, sharing the Nobel Prize in Physics, in 1909 and being created a Marquis (Marchese) in 1929. After rather protracted divorce proceedings, his marriage to Beatrice was annulled in February 1924 but on 12 June 1927, he married for a second time. His bride was the Countess Maria Cristina Bezzi-Scali, the daughter of a noble Papal family. Their daughter, born on 20 July 1930, was christened Maria Elettra Elena Anna by Cardinal Pacelli.

Marconi was diagnosed in 1927 as having a serious heart condition and during the early 1930s, he experienced a number of heart attacks. He was granted an audience with the Pope on 17 July 1937 and three days later, while still in Rome, he suffered a major heart attack and died at the age of sixty four. He was given a state funeral in Rome and at the hour of his funeral, most radio services throughout the world remained silent for a few minutes, as a mark of respect.

4. Bridging the Atlantic Ocean

Marconi faced up to the challenge of bridging the Atlantic Ocean with a combination of enthusiasm, determination, patience and tenacity. Many a lesser man would have wilted in the face of so many problems and disappointments but he was prepared to work hard, night and day, and expected his team to do the same. He realised that he would need a transmitter with considerably more power than those in use at his coast stations, if he was to signal successfully over a distance of about 4500km. He would be working at the frontiers of technology and the cost of such a scheme could be crippling.

The Company had just appointed Dr J.A. Fleming, Professor of Electrical Technology at the University College, London, as its scientific adviser and in July 1900, Marconi gave him the task of designing and building the transatlantic transmitter. Fleming was well acquainted with the works of Maxwell and Hertz and, even more relevant to Marconi's requirements, he had extensive practical experience of high-voltage, alternating-current power plant.

A suitable site for the British station was leased at Poldhu, near Mullion, in Cornwall and preliminary site work commenced in October 1900. A small coast station was also installed on the Lizard peninsula, 9km from Poldhu, to cooperate in local tests with the larger station. Work progressed rapidly at both stations and initial testing had started by late January 1901. Poldhu was the first of a new generation of transmitters and the conventional battery power supply was replaced by a 25 kilowatt (kW) alternator, driven by a large oil engine. The alternator produced an output of 2000 volts, 50 Hertz, which was stepped up to 20,000 volts in a transformer and applied successively across two spark gaps and associated oscillatory circuits. The second of these formed part of the aerial circuit. Slow-speed keying of the transmitter, using a heavy and well-insulated Morse key, varied the alternator output circuit. The large aerial consisted of 400 vertical wires, arranged in the form of an inverted cone, 61 metres in height, supported from a circle of twenty poles.

In those early days, there was no means of measuring radio frequencies but it was estimated that Poldhu was operating on a frequency of 820kHz, equivalent to a wavelength of 366 metres.

Construction work at Poldhu was well advanced by March 1901 and Marconi left for New York, accompanied by R.N. Vyvyan, the senior engineer at Poldhu. A suitable site for the corresponding American station was found at South Wellfleet, Cape Cod, Massachusetts and Marconi then returned to London, leaving Vyvyan to organise and supervise the construction of the Cape Cod station. In June, test transmissions from Poldhu, using a temporary aerial, produced clear signals at a coast station in Niton, on the Isle of Wight, which had replaced the station at the Needles Hotel.

In a severe storm, on 17 September 1901, with the large aerial not quite completed, all the masts collapsed at Poldhu but within a few days, another temporary aerial had been erected there. The aerial at Cape Cod suffered a similar fate in November. With the temporary aerial in use at Poldhu, the signals received at the newly-opened coast station at Crookhaven, County Cork, were strong enough to encourage Marconi to go and listen for them on the other side of the Atlantic Ocean. Crookhaven was 360km from Poldhu and the successful transmission proved that the radiated wave was following the earth's curvature, contrary to the predictions of the theorists. Marconi was in quite a predicament, having lost the use of both his large aerials. Under the circumstances, he was obliged to curb his ambitions and decided to carry out listening tests only, at a point in North America as near as possible to Poldhu. The obvious location was in Newfoundland and Marconi and his team arrived in St John's on 6 December. He chose a site on Signal Hill, about 180 metres above the harbour, not far from Heart's Content, where the first genuinely successful transatlantic telegraph cables had been brought ashore some 35 years earlier. Because of the temporary nature of these tests, Marconi had with him just a small selection of apparatus, including a tuned receiver and a Solari mercury detector, developed by his old school friend. This detector, also known as the Italian Navy detector, was in fact a semi-conductor rectifier and although erratic in performance, was very sensitive when used with a telephone receiver. The team also had coils of aerial wire, earth plates, large kites, balloons and the means of generating hydrogen, with which to fill the balloons. The apparatus was unpacked, checked and assembled on 9 December and a telegram sent to Fleming at Poldhu, asking for the letter 'S', in Morse code, to be transmitted at agreed times, from 11 December. In the meantime, a more permanent vertical aerial, in the shape of a large fan, had been erected at Poldhu.

On the appointed day, the aerial at Signal Hill was buffeted badly by the wind and no signal was received. Marconi decided that the movements of the aerial were producing variations in its natural capacitance, making it impossible to keep the receiver in tune. This difficulty prompted him to abandon the tuned receiver and rely on the Solari detector and headphones. The gales became more severe and a balloon was blown away. On Thursday, 12 December 1901, a kite was carried away by the wind but Marconi persisted with another kite and about 150 metres of aerial wire. That afternoon, both Marconi and Kemp heard the three dots of the letter 'S', in Morse code, several times, before the faint signals were lost in static noise. The weather became more hostile and further tests were abandoned. Neither Marconi nor Kemp could be regarded as unbiased listeners and unfortunately, there was no permanent record, such as a Morse printer tape, of the signals heard on 12 December. Nevertheless, Marconi cabled his London office with the good news and two days later he informed the press. World reaction was immediate and predictable. Some praised him for his work whilst others doubted his success, claiming that he had probably mistaken atmospheric disturbances for the Morse signals.

Marconi's experiments in Newfoundland were prematurely terminated when he received a letter from solicitors acting for the Anglo-American Telegraph Company, which had carried his telegram to London a few days earlier. The cable company asserted its monopoly in Newfoundland of all telegraphic communication and threatened him with legal action if he continued with his experiments. The Governments of Nova Scotia and of Canada then offered him land and a financial incentive to stay in Canada. After a preliminary search for a suitable site on Cape Breton Island, he visited the South Wellfleet station and then sailed home from New York, on 22 January 1902.

In the meantime, numerous modifications had been carried out to the equipment and aerial at Poldhu and on 22 February, Marconi sailed back to New York on the American Line *ss Philadelphia*. The ship had been fitted out with a 4-wire cage aerial, 57 metres above the deck, and Marconi had with him a tuned receiver, a Branly coherer and a Morse printer. His intention was to ensure that all signals received from Poldhu were recorded on the printer and witnessed by the ship's captain, who would also confirm the ship's position at the time. Strong signals were received during daylight up to a distance of 1120km from Poldhu but to everyone's surprise, it was found that the signals became stronger after the sun had set and the effective range was significantly increased. At night, signals were received at a distance of about 2500km from Poldhu and Morse 'S's at up to about 3360km. Marconi's earlier claims had been vindicated and the 'night effect' was an important scientific discovery. If he had known of this phenomenon earlier, he could have saved himself much frustration and anguish.

After disembarking in New York, Marconi visited Ottawa and then travelled to Cape Breton Island, where a site for the Canadian station was selected at Table Head, near Glace Bay. Vyvyan was moved from Cape Cod to press ahead with the construction of the Glace Bay station. This incorporated all the modifications carried out at Poldhu and the main source of power was a 75kW alternator, driven by a steam engine.

During this period, Marconi developed a new type of detector, based on an effect discovered by Professor Ernest Rutherford. This proved superior to the coherer and enabled much higher signalling speeds to be achieved. It was a magnetic device, which soon became standard equipment on ships, affectionately christened *Maggie*. Carborundum-steel detectors were introduced in 1906, followed by reliable valve receivers in 1918.

In May 1902, further important modifications were made at Poldhu and the wavelength was changed to 1100 metres. At the same time, Glace Bay and Cape Cod were redesigned to operate on wavelengths of 2000 metres. The station at Glace Bay was completed in October, but reception from Poldhu was disappointing. After a number of frustrating trials, it was decided to transmit from Glace Bay to Poldhu, taking advantage of the greater power available there. The first tests began in November but the outcome remained disappointing and unpredictable, although some signals were received at Poldhu during December and January, on a wavelength of 1650 metres.

The station at Cape Cod became operational in January 1903, its main purpose being to transmit messages from the USA to Glace Bay, a distance of 960km, for onward transmission to Poldhu. This link was found to be effective at night only but on 18 January 1903, conditions were so good that a message transmitted from Cape Cod to Glace Bay was received at Poldhu. This was the first wireless message to be received in Britain direct from the USA.

Because of the unreliability of the transatlantic service at the time, transmissions were discontinued from the end of January 1903 until the end of March, when a limited press service was provided for *The Times* newspaper, in London. This service came to an abrupt halt in early April, when an accumulation of ice brought down the aerial at Glace Bay. This incident led to the electric heating of aerials, to prevent icing.

In August 1903, Marconi sailed to New York on the Cunard Line *ss Lucania* and received news reports from Poldhu and Glace Bay throughout the voyage. The news was published in a daily news sheet and such was the success of this enterprise, that the first regular *Cunard Bulletin* was published on board the *ss Campania* on 4 June 1904. Other shipping lines soon followed, with their own transatlantic news sheets.

Most of the frustrations that Marconi and his team experienced in their tests between Poldhu, Glace Bay and Cape Cod arose from the characteristics of the propagation path. Little was known about the behaviour of the ionised layers in the ionosphere and their influence on the propagation of electromagnetic waves. Heaviside and Kennelly had published their ideas about these layers in 1902, but it was not until the 1920s that their theory gained respectability.

Throughout the summer of 1903, experiments and modifications continued at all three stations, in an attempt to overcome the propagation problems. In May 1904, it was decided that a new site should be acquired at Glace Bay, to enable a larger aerial to be erected there, operating on a longer wavelength. Because of legal delays, the new site did not become available until November. The aerial took the form of an elaborate umbrella of 200 wires, supported by a large number of masts.

The new Glace Bay station became available for tests in May 1905 and the redesigned aerial produced an improvement in performance. In June 1905, successful communication was established with Poldhu in both directions, in daylight, on a wavelength of 3660 metres. This achievement was soon eclipsed by Marconi's discovery that quite simple aerials, consisting of long, horizontal wires and operating at even longer wavelengths, were much more effective than the elaborate and costly aerials that he had been using. The horizontal wires, however, had to be considerably longer than the down lead. This new aerial, known as the inverted-L or bent aerial, was found to have pronounced directional properties and its performance was enhanced by aligning it in the direction of the distant station. The new aerial at Glace Bay was immediately modified and the signal received at Poldhu improved significantly.

The site at Poldhu was too restricted to allow the construction of a long inverted-L aerial there and it later became an experimental centre for the development of short-wave services, until it was closed in 1934.

The Company decided that a new site was required as the UK terminal of the transatlantic service and the west coast of Ireland had the attraction of being the nearest spot in Britain to Glace Bay. After a series of tests, the choice fell on Clifden, in Galway. Preliminary site work began in October 1905 and in that year, Fleming developed a wavemeter, which could be used to measure radio frequencies.

The design of the station at Clifden included all the new

techniques that had proved successful elsewhere. The aerial was of the inverted–L design, running in the direction of the Glace Bay station and operating on a wavelength of 6666 metres, equivalent to 45kHz. The generating plant was rated at 300kW and provided a direct-current output, to charge a bank of 6000 secondary storage cells. With the cells alone, the station supply voltage was allowed to fall to as low as 11,000 volts but with a generator connected across the supply, the voltage increased to 15,000 volts. The generators were driven by steam turbines, which were powered from peat-fired boilers and the Company ran its own light railway, to carry peat to the station from the surrounding bogs.

By 1906, the number of spark-gap transmitters in use had increased greatly and the degree of selectivity offered by the receivers was proving to be inadequate. Marconi saw the need for a transmitter which operated at a single frequency, so that a receiver tuned sharply to that frequency would not be troubled by interference from other transmitters.

To achieve his aim, he designed and produced an unusual machine, known as a disc discharger. This machine generated continuous oscillations at high power and at radio-frequencies up to about 200kHz. For technical reasons, these continuous oscillations of constant amplitude could not be received with the magnetic detectors which, by then, were in common use. As a result, the disc discharger had to be modified, so as to produce an audible note in the receiver.

Both Clifden and Glace Bay were equipped with these modified discs and by mid 1907, Clifden was completed and commissioning tests began. The finances of the Company and Marconi's reputation were delicately balanced when, on the morning of 15 October 1907, a number of distinguished guests were assembled on both sides of the Atlantic to witness the official opening of the new service. The operator at Clifden tapped out a message from Lord Avebury to the *New York Times* and a congratulatory message was quickly received from Glace Bay. At last, it seemed that the Company could look forward to a transatlantic service that would be reliable and commercially acceptable. A limited public telegraph service was immediately opened up between the two stations and a full service commenced in February 1908. In that month also, a modified disc discharger was installed at Cape Cod.

The Clifden service was interrupted by a serious fire at Glace Bay, in the autumn of 1909, which completely destroyed the transmitter and receivers. These were eventually replaced with the most up-to-date equipment, together with power plant similar to that at Clifden. The new receivers were located about one kilometre from the transmitter, and it was arranged that the transmitter could be controlled and keyed from the receiver building. This arrangement was later accepted as standard practice by the Company. Work continued at Glace Bay throughout the cold Canadian winter and the station was reopened in April 1910. The transmitted wavelength at Clifden was increased to 6000 metres in September.

It was customary at the time to instal a transmitter and receiver on the same site, but the strong field of the local transmitter swamped the weak signals incoming from the distant transmitter. For this reason, a transmitter had to be shut down when its local receiver was brought into use. This Simplex method of working was inefficient and an arrangement of aerials was developed which enabled a transmitter and its local receiver to be used simultaneously, in a Duplex system.

The Clifden receivers were moved to Letterfrack, about 11km away, in 1911 and the new type receiving aerials were installed there. Similar aerials were provided for the Glace Bay receivers, when they were moved some 20km to a new site at Louisbourg and brought into use in 1913.

Two directional aerials were provided at each of the receiving stations. One was aligned on the distant transmitter to receive a good signal from that source, together with an interfering signal from the local transmitter. The second aerial provided a strong signal from the local transmitter. By careful adjustment and balancing of the signals from these two aerials, the unwanted local signal was eliminated, leaving a clear signal from the distant station.

The siting of the stations at Glace Bay and Clifden was influenced at the time by an overriding need to make the propagation path between them as short as possible. The remoteness of the sites from the terminal stations in London, New York and Montreal was of lesser significance. Technological improvements, however, had made the length of the propagation path less critical and as a consequence, the wireless stations could be sited nearer to their circuit terminals. Soon after the reopening of the new Glace Bay station in 1910, it was realised that the land lines from Glace Bay to New York were constantly overloaded with traffic, much of it of a less urgent local nature. With no priority given to the wireless messages, delays of up to twelve hours could occur in their arrival in New York. The *New York Times* carried out an exercise in which the land lines were cleared of all local traffic for a brief period and under those conditions, the message time from London to New York was found to be a commendable ten minutes.

An analysis of the service provided on the transatlantic route showed that most of the traffic was between London and New York. It was also realised that the long land lines between the wireless stations and the terminal stations were very vulnerable to storm damage, causing frequent loss of service. These revelations convinced the Company that a direct service was justified between London and New York, with shorter land-line connections and it was decided to locate the wireless stations as near as possible to London and New York.

The site chosen for the British transmitter was close to the village of Waunfawr, near Caernarfon, in North Wales, with

William Henry Preece c.1890

(photo: Eunice Williams)

Bryn Helen, Caernarfon – the birthplace of William Preece

(photo: David Williams)

Penrhos, Caeathro

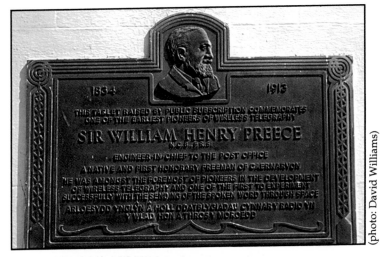

(photo: David Williams)

A bronze tablet, fitted into the wall of the Head Post Office
building in Caernarfon, on the initiative of the Borough Council
and the town's Rotary Club unveiled in April 1953 by
Sir W.H. Preece's two surviving daughters, Amy and Mary.

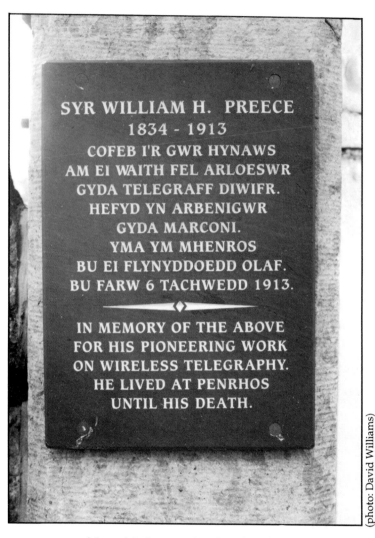

SYR WILLIAM H. PREECE
1834 - 1913
COFEB I'R GWR HYNAWS
AM EI WAITH FEL ARLOESWR
GYDA TELEGRAFF DIWIFR.
HEFYD YN ARBENIGWR
GYDA MARCONI.
YMA YM MHENROS
BU EI FLYNYDDOEDD OLAF.
BU FARW 6 TACHWEDD 1913.

IN MEMORY OF THE ABOVE
FOR HIS PIONEERING WORK
ON WIRELESS TELEGRAPHY.
HE LIVED AT PENRHOS
UNTIL HIS DEATH.

(photo: David Williams)

Memorial plaque at Penrhos, Caeathro

(photo: GEC – Marconi Ltd.)

Marconi and his early apparatus, 1896

(photo: GEC – Marconi Ltd.)

Post Office Engineers checking Marconi equipment.
Bristol Channel demonstration 1897.

View looking up the entry drive to radio station, 1912.
Waunfawr, early construction stage.

(photo: GEC – Marconi Ltd.)

Waunfawr aerial nearing completion. Early 1914.

(photo: GEC – Marconi Ltd.)

View of the power house and the transmitter house,
Waunfawr, 1912, early construction stage

Waunfawr valve transmitter.
Aerial tuning inductance and ratio winding.

Waunfawr valve transmitter 1921

(photo: GEC – Marconi Ltd.)

The power house, Waunfawr 1912

Main station – Tywyn.
Main building, power house and lattice mast frame aerial.

High-frequency receiving circuits, Tywyn

(photo: GEC – Marconi Ltd.)

Main station – Tywyn.
Wireless operating room, with automatic transmitters,
perforators, hand key and receiving telephones.

(photo: Electronics World)

Pioneer operators at Tywyn wireless station.
Top row: Misses W.F. Bruton, A.V. Edgar, D.M. Jarred and
F.M. Rogers. Bottom row: Misses E.A. Pugh, M. Beresford,
R. Perry, G.A. March and M. Murphy.

The receiving room at Tywyn

(photo: GEC – Marconi Ltd.)

Auxiliary room at Tywyn c.1918

(photo: GEC – Marconi Ltd.)

Early days: Italian princess sees where her father pioneered radio

Royal visit by Marconi daughter

By NEVILLE JONES

THE VISIT of an Italian princess to Gwynedd revived memories of the early days of radio.

Elettra Marconi visited the old transmitting station at Cefn Du, Waunfawr, where her father, radio pioneer Guglielmo Marconi, developed much of his pioneering work.

Her visit on Tuesday was arranged by Cyfeillion Marconi, which is organised by Llanrug and Waunfawr Community Councils, Artur Waunfawr and Dragon Radio.

During a visit to Gwynedd Council Offices, Princess Elettra, of Rome, said: "This is my first visit to an area to help Caernarfon's Sir William Preece gave him was vital.

"I remember my father as a wonderful, loving parent, and both my mother and I loved him greatly."

Elettra Marconi holds the title La Principessa through her mother, Countess Maria Cristina Bezzi Scali, Guglielmo Marconi was her second husband.

Princess Elettra said: "My mother wrote a book in Italian about my father. When it is translated, I hope to come back to Caernarfon to promote it."

Her present visit was originally planned for Holyhead, where Marconi also developed his work, but was extended to include the Caernarfon area.

She was presented with a plaque to commemorate the visit, on behalf of Cyfeillion Marconi, by Mayor of Caernarfon, Coun Jack Thomas.

He said: "She was very approachable. My wife hit it off very well with her."

Princess Elettra was shown a bronze replica of a monument at Wahroonga, New South Wales, commemorating the 80th anniversary of Marconi's first transmission from Cefn Du to Australia.

Dewi Roberts, chairman of the Dragon Amateur Radio Club, said: "Princess Elettra's visit is of great importance due to all the local connections."

She also visited Caernarfon Castle and William Preece's old home at Caeathro.

Royal chat: Princess Elettra Marconi (left) meets Dewi Roberts, of Llanfairpwll, under the gaze of Barbara Anzioni, arranger of the visit to Holyhead.

(98 07 AR 416 27)

Mercurial meeting: Coun and Mrs Jack Thomas (left); chairman of Gwynedd Council Coun John James; and Princess Elettra admire the Wahroonga statuette, resplendent with Mercury, god of communication.

(98 07 AR 416 31)

(photo: Arwyn Roberts)

(photo: GEC – Marconi Ltd.)

*The wireless room of RMS Olympic 1911
similar to that on Titanic*

(photo: GEC – Marconi Ltd.)

Elettra moored at Penzance – Cornwall

(photo: GEC – Marconi Ltd.)

Marconi beam station at Dorchester, England – used for services to north and south America, Egypt and the Far East

(photo: GEC – Marconi Ltd.)

A short-wave beam aerial system.
Radiators on the right and reflectors on the left.

an associated receiving station at Tywyn, some 60km in a line due south, on Cardigan Bay. The corresponding American stations were located at Tuckerton and New Brunswick, some 96km apart, in the State of New Jersey.

Construction of the Waunfawr station began in 1912 and it was brought into use in 1914. It took over some of the Clifden services when that station was put out of action in July 1922 (and later abandoned), during the Irish troubles. The Waunfawr station remained the most important long-wave wireless-telegraph station in Britain until it was eclipsed by the Post Office high-power station at Hillmorton, near Rugby, which opened in January 1926.

By the end of 1918, thermionic valves became available, which operated effectively at very high radio frequencies and C.S. Franklin, of the Marconi Company, was given the task of setting up and operating a short-wave transmitter at the Poldhu experimental station. This had a power input rating of 12kW and transmitted on wavelengths of between 5 and 100 metres. Experiments were also conducted with various designs of short-wave aerials, with and without reflectors. Transmissions from Poldhu produced favourable reports from a number of monitoring points around the world, as far apart as Australia, Canada and South America, all testifying to the strength of the signals at certain times, during a 24-hour period.

At that stage, Marconi decided that he needed a floating laboratory, so that he could sail to distant oceans to monitor the short-wave transmissions from Poldhu. At the end of 1919, he purchased the *Rowanski*, a luxury steam yacht of about 700 tons, that had been built at Leith for Archduke Stefan of Austria. At the outbreak of World War One, the British Admiralty had commandeered this ship, for use by the Royal Navy. Marconi had the ship repaired and fitted out at Birkenhead and she was renamed *Elettra*. She set out on her first cruise, to the Mediterranean, in the spring of 1920 and, as was to become his custom, Marconi entertained members of his family and special friends on this 'working' cruise.

In addition to the standard long-wave wireless equipment, the ship also carried a variety of short-wave equipment and related scientific instruments to measure radio frequencies and signal strengths. Tests carried out from Poldhu confirmed the merits of long-distance, short-wave transmissions, although their greater tendency to fading was to present a technical challenge for some years.

The Marconi Company pressed on with the development of short-wave services, and in 1924 was awarded a contract by the British Government to set up its short-wave beam system, linking London telegraphically with the major member countries of the British Empire; Australia, Canada, India and South Africa. A similar link was also planned between London and New York. All the stations at the British end were then taken over and run by the BPO which, in 1928, brought into use a short-wave radio telephone link between London and New York.

The success of the beam services resulted in a significant loss of revenue for the transoceanic telegraph-cable companies, and also for some Dominion Governments that had subsidised them. In 1928, the British Government convened an Imperial Wireless and Cable Conference, at which it was agreed that the cable and beam wireless services should merge, creating a company to be called the Imperial and International Communications Ltd. This was formed in 1929, changing its name in 1934 to Cable and Wireless Ltd. As a result, the BPO lost control of the beam telegraph stations in 1929, but retained its monopoly of radio-telephone services. At the same time, the Marconi Company lost all its wireless stations and was left as a research and manufacturing organisation.

Short-wave transmitters consumed only a fraction of the power required by the old long-wave stations and the aerials were generally simpler and less expensive to construct. The location of these stations no longer required the large tracts of land demanded by the long-wave, inverted-L aerials.

The rapid growth in short-wave services, particularly of radio telephony, precipitated the demise of the long-wave stations. The station at Waunfawr had a stay of execution until a solution was found for the troublesome propagation problems on the transatlantic route. These problems had been effectively resolved by the mid 1930s and the station was closed down in 1939, a victim of the progress of technology.

The receiving station at Tywyn, from where the Waunfawr station was controlled, remained in use until 1923, when its services were transferred to a new, centralised, receiving station at Brentwood, in Essex. The Waunfawr transmitters were then controlled from the Company's new Central Telegraph Office at Radio House, Wilson Street, London.

5. The Stations in Wales

5.1 The Waunfawr Transmitting Station

The site chosen for the Marconi Company's new transatlantic transmitting station, on the UK mainland, was on the west-facing slope of Cefndu mountain, in Caernarfonshire, and its construction began in 1912. The site was officially designated as the Caernarfon station but in North Wales it was better known as the Waunfawr station.

The station buildings were located at a height of 207 metres above sea level and included a two-storey residential block, for members of staff who had been brought in from afar. This building contained 16 bedrooms, a kitchen and dining room, a smoking-lounge and other amenities, which helped to soften the impact of their environment on newcomers to the district. The main building was divided into two sections, the transmitter hall and the experimental section, where Marconi developed new machines and equipment. Two soundproof chambers for the disc dischargers were located next to the transmitter hall and various other rooms, including an office for the shift engineer, were located behind these.

Heavy machinery and materials were brought to the site entrance on freight vehicles, where they were unloaded, as the transport of these items from the Ceunant road up the mountainside was made difficult by the boggy nature of the ground. To overcome this problem, a light railway was laid from the road up towards the furthest boundary of the site and the heavy freight was carried along these rails on small trucks. The line was divided into three sections, each with its own stationary steam engine and wire-rope haulage system, which pulled the trucks up the slope. Foundations and stay anchors for the aerial masts, alone, required the transport of about 6000 tonnes of material.

The original aerial, which was of the inverted-L design, ran for about 1100 metres up the gently-sloping mountainside. It was made up of 32 silicon-bronze wires, which fanned out gradually up the slope, the far end being some 213 metres higher than the lower end. The average width of the aerial was 152 metres and it was supported from ten tubular steel, stayed masts, 122 metres high.

The earth system was made up of a number of metal plates sunk into the ground, so as to form two large circles around the main building. These were connected to other plates buried in an area that extended from immediately beneath the aerial to the eastern boundary of the site.

A 3-phase, 30,000 volt mains supply was provided by the North Wales Power Company and this was stepped down to 440 volts at the wireless station Power House. This mains power was generated at the Cwm Dyli hydro-electric power station, 14km to the south-east, on the far side of Snowdon, which had been built in 1906 to supply power to the slate industry in the Llanberis area.

The initial plant provision at Waunfawr consisted of two synchronous disc dischargers, each of which was coupled to the shaft of its own 300kW single-phase alternator. Each alternator was directly driven by a 3-phase motor connected to the 440 volt mains supply. In addition to these two rotary machines, there were also heavy items. such as tuning coils and their associated capacitors, all of which were of solid and bulky design, subjected to intense electrical stress.

In March 1914, test transmissions began between Waunfawr and the Italian Government station at Coltano, near Pisa, which had also been built by the Marconi

Company. These transmissions were on a wavelength of 5000 metres, with a current of 130 amperes in the aerial. Tests were also carried out with the Canadian receiving station at Louisbourg in April, on a wavelength of 11,140 metres by day and 5800 metres at night, and later with New Jersey.

The Mayor and Corporation of Caernarfon welcomed Marconi to a banquet at the Sportsman Hotel, in the town, on 20 May 1914. They thanked him for the honour that he had bestowed on their County, by selecting it as the location for such an important wireless station. During the banquet, a wireless message was delivered to the Mayor, which had been sent by the Glace Bay staff, in Marconi's honour.

By August 1914, a full programme of test transmissions was in progress at the Waunfawr station. This was temporarily interrupted by the outbreak of World War One but the tests were restarted at the end of September, with transmissions to Egypt and Russia. During the war, the station was taken over, first by the Post Office and then by the Admiralty but it continued to be run and operated by Marconi Company staff.

In June 1916, the two synchronous disc machines were replaced by three timed spark disc dischargers, generally known as timed discs. These rotary machines were the only ones available that could generate almost continuous waves at power outputs of about 200kW, but the noise produced by their constant spark sequence was intolerable, even though they were enclosed in soundproof chambers. Not only were the machines unpopular with those who had to work near them, but they also called for very precise and skilled adjustments. Successful tests were carried out with Coltano in September 1916, transmitting day and night on a wavelength of 11,100 metres, with an aerial current of about 220 amperes. In 1918, the wavelength was changed to 14,000 metres.

As a hint of things to come, C.S. Franklin established an

experimental short-wave radio-telephone link between the Waunfawr site and Kingston (Dun Laoghaire), about 12km south of Dublin, in 1917, on a wavelength of 15 metres. The distance involved was 125km, with a transmitter input power measured in watts rather than in kilowatts.

The aerial at Waunfawr had dual directional properties. For its designated purpose, it was aligned on the New Jersey receiving station in the USA but in its backward direction it covered Australasia. This feature was used on 22 September 1918, to transmit the very first wireless message to Australia. The sender was William Morris Hughes, Prime Minister of Australia, who was on a brief visit to Britain after calling on Australian troops at the battlefields of northern France. Hughes was Prime Minister of Australia from 1915 to 1923, and had family ties with Llandudno. The message was sent by prearrangement with Amalgamated Wireless (Australasia) Limited and was received by its Managing Director, E.T. Fisk, at his home in Wahroonga, near Sydney. The receiving equipment was designed and built by his company.

Poulsen-arc transmitters were delivered to the station in 1918, for use as emergency back-up for the disc dischargers, and they generated an aerial current of 100 amperes. Poulsen-arc machines, in general, radiated their energy over a very wide frequency band and soon became notorious for the interference that they caused to other transmissions.

By 1919, with peace restored in Europe, control of the station reverted to the Company, which had yet to establish a commercial transatlantic service between its new stations. A service to Spain was introduced in 1919 and by February 1920, the station was working on a wavelength of 14,200 metres, with an aerial current of 280 amperes. On 1 March 1920, a commercial service was at last established between Wales and New Jersey.

The original earth system at Waunfawr was buried in

rocky ground and must have presented a higher electrical resistance than was desirable. Successive transmitters produced greater aerial currents and the power wasted as heat in the earth system increased accordingly. Stories are still told in the Waunfawr district of how steam was seen to rise from the ground under the aerial, at times. Also, when snow lay on the ground, it always cleared away much more quickly from under the aerial. In the 1920s, the original buried earth system was replaced by an 'earth screen', suspended directly underneath the aerial. This consisted of a fan of 32 insulated wires, supported by steel lattice masts at an average height of about 7 metres above the ground. The screen was wider than the aerial array by about 240 metres and extended beyond it at the far end. As a result, the high-frequency resistance of the aerial was much reduced, giving a significant increase in radiated power.

During the early 1900s, a number of attempts were made to redesign the commonly-used mains alternator, normally operating at 50 hertz, so that it produced high power at radio frequencies. Frederick Alexanderson, of the American General Electric Company, was particularly successful in this quest. Two of his alternators, each rated at 200kW, were installed at the Waunfawr station towards the end of 1920. These were first used for traffic on 24 April 1921, operating on wavelengths of approximately 14,000 metres and 9600 metres respectively, with an aerial current of 330 amperes. By that time, the Poulsen arc machines were no longer in use and the days of the noisy timed discs were numbered. Plans were also made to extend the aerial a further 274 metres up the mountainside.

By 1921, the Company had gained confidence in the reliability of high-power thermionic valves and a 160kW valve transmitter was assembled at Waunfawr. This was made up of three panels, on which were mounted a total of 56 valves, with the output stage containing 30 large valves connected in parallel. The valves were cooled by a blast of cold air directed at their necks. This transmitter was brought into use at the end of August, giving an aerial current of 340 amperes. In late 1921, a prolonged period of testing began, transmitting to Australia and on 4 December, the Company invited the *Daily Mail* newspaper to send a Press message direct to its correspondent in Sydney.

The timed disc machines were taken out of service in October 1921 and the transatlantic service then relied entirely on the Alexanderson alternators. Meanwhile, tests continued with the valve transmitter but it was not until September 1922 that it was accepted for commercial traffic. In May 1923, a more powerful valve transmitter was installed, using water-cooled valves. A fire service was maintained at the station, for which a large reservoir had been constructed higher up the mountain and this ensured a plentiful supply of cooling water for the new valve transmitter. By December, this unit had replaced the earlier valve transmitter and was feeding a current of 560 amperes into the aerial. By that time, the full extension of the aerial had been completed, involving the erection of six additional masts. Early in 1924, the output power of this transmitter was enhanced by the addition of 15 water-cooled valves to its output stage.

In October, the transmitter went into service carrying commercial traffic. By the end of 1924, the continuing operation of the station relied on two Alexanderson alternators and a water-cooled valve transmitter. At that stage, it was decided to split the aerial, so that two transmitters could operate quite independently and a separate feeder was erected to connect with the section of the aerial furthest away from the transmitter building. The valve transmitter operated at 9500 metres on the aerial lower down the mountainside and an Alexanderson alternator operated at 14,000 metres on the upper aerial. In December

1924, the station transmitted the first still pictures to the USA, in a test transmission with the Radio Corporation of America (RCA). This service became commercially available between London and New York in 1926. Another valve transmitter, rated at 40kW and operating on a wavelength of 7800 metres, was commissioned in 1925, together with its own new aerial. Its wavelength was later changed to 4500 metres and it was used for services to Egypt, Glace Bay and Spain.

In 1929, the Waunfawr station was taken over by Imperial and International Communications Limited which, in 1934, became Cable and Wireless Limited. The arrival of the Marconi Company's own short-wave wireless telegraph services in 1927, and the development of radio-telephone services in the early 1930s, accelerated the demise of the Waunfawr station. It was used, as required, to provide relief during periods of heavy traffic on the Atlantic route and also when short-wave services were seriously affected by magnetic storms. It also carried facsimile services, including the transmission of documents and photographs. The station was shut down in 1939 and the site has since been used for various purposes. In recent years, the main building has been adapted as a mountaineering centre and a riding school operates on the lower slopes of Cefndu. One aerial lead-out insulator can still be seen on the side of the main building and some of the mast and stay foundations remain intact. In April each year, on International Marconi Day, members of the North Wales based Dragon Amateur Radio Club operate from the site, making contact with other radio clubs, worldwide.

In late July 1998, Marconi's daughter, Princess Elettra, visited both the Waunfawr site and that of Marconi's coast radio station at Holyhead. Her journey to Waunfawr took her past Sir William Preece's home at Penrhos, Caeathro, and during a busy tour of the Caernarfon and Anglesey area, she attended a number of functions and civic receptions.

Marconi's memory is kept alive in North Wales by the Friends of Marconi (Cyfeillion Marconi), a group of enthusiasts from a number of interested organisations, such as the Dragon Amateur Radio Club and Waunfawr Venture (Antur Waunfawr). They also perpetuate the memory of Sir William Preece, who did so much to assist and encourage Marconi at the very start of his career. The Friends also played a leading role in organising Princess Elettra's visit to North Wales in July 1998 and it is their intention to open a small museum in Waunfawr, to record and preserve the history of the Cefndu station.

5.2 The Tywyn Receiving Station

The new UK receiving station was located on the outskirts of Tywyn, on the edge of Cardigan Bay. The station buildings were situated about thirty metres above sea level, at Hafod y Bryn, and the aerials ran along the steeply ascending Escuan Hill, not far from Escuan Hall. The main aerial was of the horizontal directional type, supported on five lattice-steel masts, 91 metres in height. It was aligned with the American transmitter in New Jersey, running in an easterly direction for a distance of about 3km. At its distant end, it rose to about 430 metres above sea level. A reserve aerial ran parallel to the main aerial, also for 3km, supported on 36 wooden masts each some 10 metres high. Balancing aerials, supported at a height of 24 metres, ran at right angles to the main aerial. These were tuned to the Waunfawr signal and by careful local adjustments, interference generated in the main aerial by the unwanted Waunfawr signal was cancelled out. In 1920, these aerials were all replaced by a more efficient system, developed by C.S. Franklin, which was based on the use of two Bellini-Tosi loop aerials. These were also aligned with the New Jersey transmitter and interference from any other direction was negligible.

In July 1914, the American station in New Jersey started transmitting to Tywyn on a wavelength of 11,000 metres. At Tywyn, the received signals passed from the tuned aerial to carborundum-steel detectors, a reliable form of crystal detector, and then, as audible notes, to the operator's headphones. The crystal detector limited the amplitude of sudden impulses of atmospheric noise, thus safeguarding the operator's hearing. By 1919, the carborundum detectors had been replaced by valve circuits, in which the signal from the aerial passed through a high-frequency valve amplifier before being applied to the detector stage. The rectified output was then amplified in a low-frequency amplifier, to give an audible signal at the receiver output.

With the development of high-speed signalling, electro-mechanical instruments were introduced, which enabled the receiver output signal to be recorded and then transcribed at low speed. An early device, used at Tywyn, was a dictaphone-type machine, in which the signals were recorded as fine grooves on the wax surface of a rapidly rotating cylinder. The cylinder was then re-run at a lower speed, so that the message could be manually transcribed on to punched tape. These machines were cheap to run and the wax surface was quickly cleaned up, by placing the cylinder in a cylinder-shaving machine, which removed a thin surface layer of wax.

A later instrument, known as an undulator, traced the received signal as an undulating ink line on a moving paper tape. The tape was then cut into sections and gummed on to plain paper forms, to be read by the operator and converted into punched tape in a perforator.

The electrical power requirements of the equipment at Tywyn were quite modest and were met from lead-acid storage batteries. These were charged periodically by means of a small engine-generator set.

The demands of World War One produced a shortage of male telegraphists and in 1916, the Marconi Company recruited and trained a number of female telegraphists, to work at the receiving stations. At the time, this was quite a revolutionary development, especially as they were expected to work a 24-hour shift rota. Nine of these operators were employed at Tywyn from 1916 onwards.

In addition to operating as a receiving station, Tywyn was also the control unit for the Waunfawr transmitters. The receiving operator sat close to the transmitting operator and a similar arrangement existed in New Jersey. As a result of this close association, if either receiving operator recognised a garbled message, the transmitting operator could immediately call on the distant station to repeat the message. Under adverse propagation conditions, many requests could be made for retransmission before the receiving operator was satisfied that a readable message had been recorded.

Transatlantic telegrams, destined to be transmitted by wireless, were received at the Marconi Company's office in London, where they were passed on to the instrument room. There, an operator converted the message into Morse code on a punched tape and this was then transmitted at high speed over a land line to Tywyn. At Tywyn, the message was automatically converted on to a punched tape, which was used to control the keying of the Waunfawr transmitter, again over a land line. In the receive direction, punched tape originating at Tywyn was transmitted to the Company's London office, where it produced a tape printed in Morse code characters. These were read off by an operator, who typed the message on to a telegram form and sent it on to its destination.

Improvements to the wireless equipment at all the stations eventually enabled telegraph speeds over the transatlantic link to catch up with those over the inland network, and speeds of 100 words per minute became commonplace.

Initially, the land lines to and from Tywyn terminated at the Company's Central Telegraph Office in Fenchurch Street, London but during the summer of 1922, this office was replaced by a larger centre at Radio House, Wilson Street, London. In 1923, long-wave reception for the transatlantic service was transferred from Tywyn to a central receiving station in Brentwood, Essex and the Waunfawr transmitters were then controlled from the new Central Telegraph Office at Radio House.

The Tywyn station ceased operating on 26 March 1923 and sometime later, staff accommodation, known as Marconi Bungalows, became available to local applicants. More recently, the main building was converted into two dwellings, also for local applicants, and the remains of mast and stay foundations are still to be seen in the locality.

6. Technical Notes

6.1 The Hertz Transmitter

Heinrich Daniel Ruhmkorff, a maker of scientific instruments, working in Paris, developed the induction coil in 1853, as a means of generating pulses of high voltage. As seen in Fig.1.1, this consisted of a transformer T, with a high step-up ratio and with heavy insulation, to withstand very high voltages. It also included an inbuilt automatic interrupter I, similar to that in a buzzer, which was operated by the magnetic field set up in the transformer core by the primary current. The interrupted primary current produced pulses of very high voltages in the secondary winding. A later refinement was the addition of a spark-quench capacitor C, across the interrupter contacts, to improve the device's performance and to reduce the wearing away of the contacts.

The symbols used to represent an induction coil in early circuit diagrams may seem confusing to a modern-day reader. Two of the most generally used symbols are shown in Fig.1.2, where the presence of the interrupter contacts is implied by the use of the term 'induction coil', rather than 'transformer'.

From about 1883, Hertz conducted a number of experiments, seeking to prove Maxwell's theories. At first, he used quite simple laboratory-type apparatus but in 1888 he improved his generator of electromagnetic waves, by including an induction coil in the circuit. As seen in Fig.1.3,

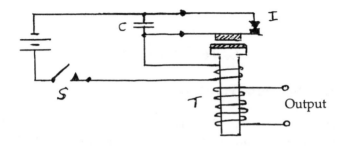

Fig.1.1. – Induction Coil (1854)

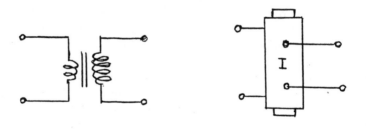

Fig.1.2 – Induction Coil Symbols

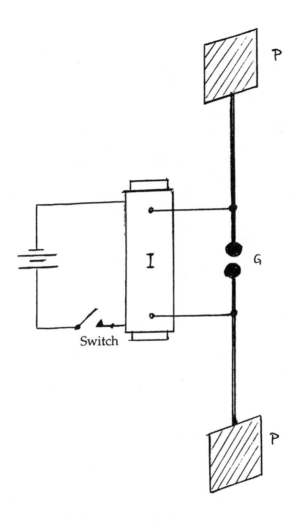

Fig.1.3 – Hertz Transmitter (1888)

the induction coil output is connected to two metal rods, the inner ends of which each terminate in a small brass sphere. These are separated by a spark gap G, of a few millimetres, and the outer end of each rod carries a large metal plate P. These two plates form a Hertzian dipole and the complete arrangement is, in fact, a transmitter.

With the switch closed, to energise the induction coil, a series of sparks jumped across the spark gap, producing sudden changes in the electric and magnetic fields in the air space between the dipoles. As a result, electromagnetic waves were radiated into space, which Hertz detected with a simple device called a Hertzian Resonator. This consisted of a large loop of thick wire, fitted with an adjustable spark gap across its two free ends. When the resonator was held a short distance from the energised transmitter, sparks were produced in its spark gap.

6.2 Marconi's Early Apparatus

Marconi modified Hertz's transmitter, so that he could switch it on and off under the control of a Morse key. He also developed a simple receiver, using a Branly coherer, which replaced the Hertzian Resonator. A small, sensitive relay was included in the coherer circuit and this was energised by the current from a single dry cell, when the coherer went into its low-resistance state. The relay current was limited to one milliamp, so as to protect the filings in the coherer. At first, the relay was used to operate a Morse printer but later, it also energised a small hammer device, not unlike an electric bell without the gongs, which tapped lightly against the coherer tube. In this way, the filings were decohered quickly, as soon as the influence of the incoming signal had faded away, resulting in an increase in signalling speed. For rather obvious reasons, the electric-bell type device was known as a tapper or decoherer. Simple

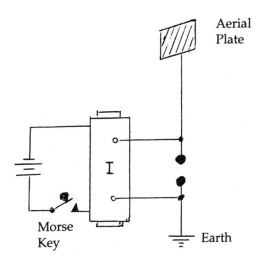

Fig.2.1 – Early Transmitter (1895)

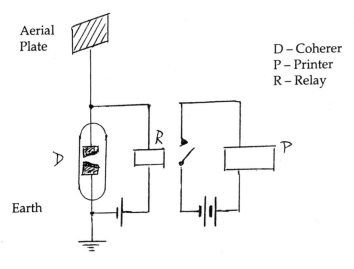

D – Coherer
P – Printer
R – Relay

Fig.2.2 – Early Receiver (1895)

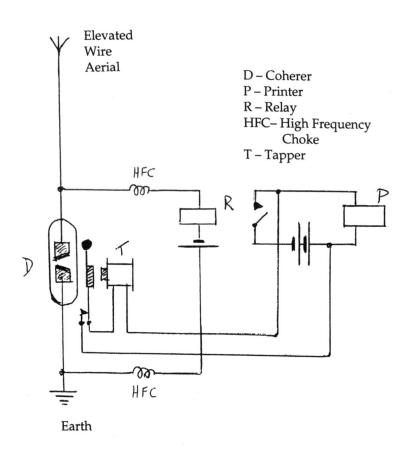

Elevated
Wire
Aerial

D – Coherer
P – Printer
R – Relay
HFC– High Frequency
        Choke
T – Tapper

Earth

Fig.2.3 – Receiver with Tapper (1896)

diagrams of these changes, carried out during 1895 and 1896, are shown in Figs.2.1, 2.2. and 2.3.

6.3 Tuning

With the increase in the number of spark transmitters in use, it became necessary to tune both transmitters and receivers, so as to reduce interference in a receiver located within range of more than one transmitter. Receiver sensitivity improved significantly in 1897, when a small, high-frequency transformer, known at the time as a *Jigger*, was used to couple the aerial to the coherer, as shown in Fig.3.1. Before long, aerial coupling coils were also used in transmitters and both transmitters and receivers became available, tuned to one particular frequency. By 1900, receivers were produced which could be tuned continuously over a limited range of frequencies and the simultaneous tuning of a number of stages in a receiver was simplified in 1904, when Franklin invented the ganged, air-spaced, variable capacitor.

Edwin H. Armstrong, who was with the American Army in Paris at the time, invented the superheterodyne receiver in 1917. This advanced receiver offered considerable improvements in sensitivity and selectivity but it came too late for the receiving station at Tywyn.

6.4 The Magnetic Detector

Neither Marconi's improved coherer nor Solari's mercury detector proved ideal in commercial use. The signalling speed of the former was limited by the need to decohere the device and the latter was unreliable. In the mid 1890s, Rutherford demonstrated that a magnetised steel needle

T – Aerial Transformer (Jigger)
D – Coherer
R – Relay
P – Printer
HFC – High Frequency Chokes

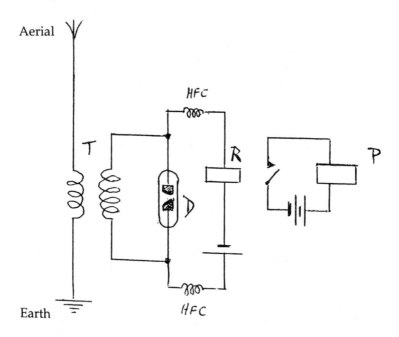

Fig.3.1 – Receiver with Aerial Transformer (1897)

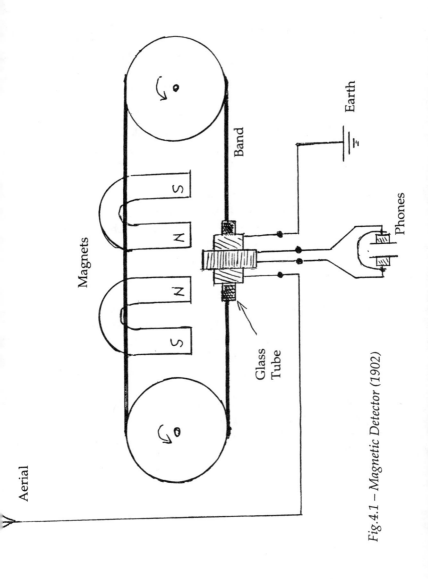

Aerial

Magnets

S

N

N

S

Band

Glass
Tube

Earth

Phones

Fig. 4.1 – Magnetic Detector (1902)

could be demagnetised by the electromagnetic field generated by a spark discharge. Marconi developed a practical use for this phenomenon and in 1902, he patented two types of magnetic detectors. Only one of these proved successful, becoming the standard Marconi detector aboard ship for many years.

The operation of this detector can be followed from Fig.4.1. An endless band of fine insulated iron wire is wrapped around two slowly-rotating wooden pulleys. The band passes through a short glass tube, which is located under the poles of two horse-shoe magnets. Similar poles of each magnet are positioned adjacent to each other over the centre of the glass tube. The other poles are then over the band but beyond the ends of the glass tube. A coil of insulated copper wire is wound over the glass tube and connected to aerial and earth as shown. A second copper-wire coil is wound over the centre section of the first coil and connected to a telephone receiver.

With no signals in the aerial coil, the iron wire becomes partly magnetised within the glass tube but the lines of force are distorted by the slow movement of the band. When a signal is received in the aerial coil, the magnetic field in the iron wire becomes rearranged, inducing a voltage in the second coil, thus generating a sound in the telephone receiver.

When correctly set, this detector was superior to the coherer and its robust design made it an ideal choice for ship-board use. Because of its sharper output, with no need to decohere, higher signalling speeds were possible.

6.5 The Poldhu Transmitter

To generate the high power required for the proposed transatlantic link, Fleming decided initially on a two-stage arrangement for his transmitter, a simplified circuit of which is shown in Fig.5.1. This design was later modified a number of times during test transmissions.

When the signalling key K is closed, transformer T1 steps up the full alternator voltage to 20kV. This is applied across C1 and at a critical voltage, a spark passes across the gap G1, thus discharging C1. The oscillatory current produced in the primary of the high-frequency transformer T2, in turn, charges C2. Again, at a critical voltage, a spark passes across G2, discharging C2 and setting up a damped oscillatory current in the primary of a second high-frequency transformer T3, which produces oscillations in the aerial.

The efficient operation of the transmitter depended on the correct tuning of the oscillatory circuits and with the high currents and voltages present in these circuits, care had to be taken to prevent voltage surges from damaging the plant. The two oscillatory capacitors, C1 and C2, consisted of a number of units, each made up of twenty large glass plates, coated on one side with tinfoil and held in stoneware containers filled with linseed oil, which formed a self-healing dielectric. Because of the very high voltages involved, these capacitors were very solidly built and occupied a large amount of floor space. The high-frequency transformers, T2 and T3, were also of heavy construction, to withstand the stresses imposed on them by the electrical field. For the initial tests, the primary spark gap G1 was set at 7.5 millimetres and the secondary gap G2 at 40 millimetres.

The keying of the transmitter presented Fleming with a serious problem, because of the high current that had to be interrupted, with the attendant risk of high self-induced voltages being generated. After experimenting with a number of arrangements, he finally settled on the addition of a high-inductance choke in the primary circuit of T1. The operation of the key K short-circuited the choke L1, allowing

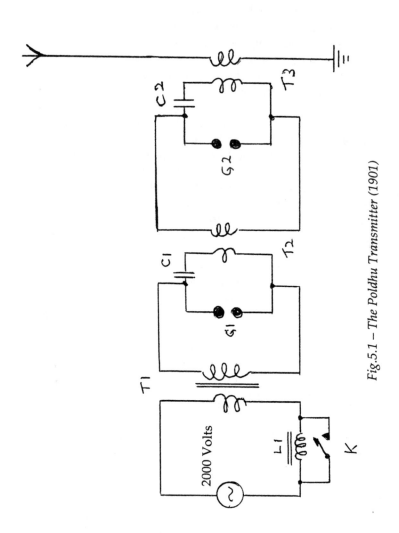

Fig.5.1 – The Poldhu Transmitter (1901)

the full alternator output voltage to reach T1. The key was at a point of high potential and in the interest of safety, and also to prepare for the remote keying of transmitters, the key was later placed in a low-voltage circuit, where it operated an intermediate high-voltage relay, which keyed the transmitter.

Fleming estimated the transmitter output power to be about 10 to 12kW but he had no means of measuring its fundamental radiated frequency, which remained a matter of controversy. In a lecture at the Royal Institution in March 1908, Marconi quoted the wavelength as 366 metres (820kHz) but some remained convinced that it was somewhere between 2000 and 3000 metres.*

* Wavelength, in metres = $\dfrac{3 \times 10^8}{\text{Frequency, in Hertz}}$

6.6 The Disc Discharger

Marconi's original disc discharger generated an almost continuous wave, but this could not be received by the magnetic detector. He then added studs to the periphery of the main disc, to produce the modified disc, in which the spark was interrupted, or modulated, as the disc revolved at high speed. This produced a musical note in the receiver, at a frequency that was dependent on the speed of rotation of the disc and on the number of studs. These early disc dischargers were energised from a direct-current power supply of 12kV, which relied on the use of 6000 secondary storage cells. This plant was costly both to instal and to maintain, and was later superseded by the introduction of the synchronous disc discharger.

In this machine, the disc was energised from a single-phase alternator feeding into a step-up transformer, to give a supply of 10-15kV. The alternator was fitted with up to 12 pairs of poles, and was keyed on to the same shaft as the disc. Both were driven at a speed of 2000 revolutions per minute, by a 3-phase electric motor. The disc, which was insulated from the shaft, had a diameter of about one metre and was fitted with a heavy rim of brass or copper. Copper studs, equal in number to the number of poles on the alternator, were fitted at equal spacing around its rim.

As the disc rotated, the studs swept past two copper spark electrodes, the position of which could be adjusted relative to the rotation of the disc, so as to synchronise the machine. The spark electrodes were aligned so that they were opposite two adjacent studs at the instant that the energising voltage reached its peak value, in each half cycle.

The basic principles of operation of a synchronous disc discharger can be followed from Fig.6.1. For clarity, only four studs have been shown on the disc. The alternator G and insulated disc D are keyed to the same shaft. The switch K represents the contacts of a key-controlled high-voltage relay. When K is closed, the capacitor C is charged and at the peak voltage, sparks jump across the two gaps between the electrodes E and studs S, thus discharging C through the primary winding of the aerial coupling coil J. Further rotation of the disc quenches the spark, assisted by a blast of compressed air in the larger machines. A rapid sequence of heavily damped sparks is thus generated during the closure of K, which shock excites the aerial. The tuned aerial is only slightly damped, so that the oscillations persist in it at its natural frequency. The dots and dashes of the Morse code are recognised in the receiver as musical notes, at twice the frequency of the alternator.

A further development of the disc discharger was the timed spark discharger, generally known as the timed disc. The synchronous disc discharger produced trains of gradually diminishing oscillations in the aerial. If a number

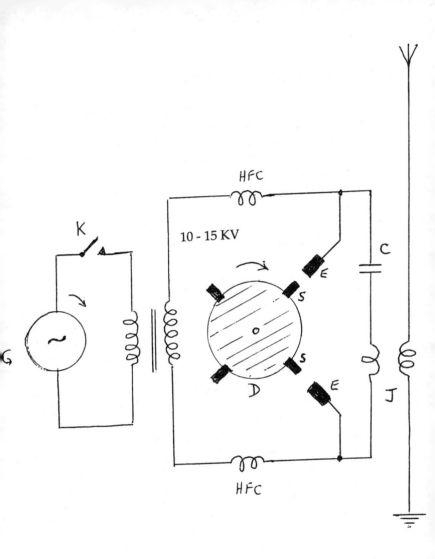

Fig.6.1 – Synchronous Disc Discharger (1909)

of these discs could be arranged so that each discharged in turn, through its own tuned circuit, into a common aerial circuit, then by controlling the phase and timing of each discharge, a more powerful and sustained output could be achieved. In this machine, two studded discs were mounted on a common shaft, each with two sets of spark electrodes, thus providing four independent primary circuits. A third, smaller disc, known as the timing disc, ensured the accurate timing of the main spark discharges, by means of a trigger spark.

6.7 The Poulsen Arc Generator

William Duddell, an English scientist, discovered in the late 1890s that a carbon arc could be made to generate an audible musical note. Valdemar Poulsen, working in America, extended the range of Duddell's musical arc so as to produce radio frequencies and in 1903, he patented his carbon arc as a generator of continuous electromagnetic waves, at high power.

A carbon arc has negative-resistance characteristics that contradict Ohm's Law. The voltage across the arc rises if the current in it falls, and falls if the current rises. The basic operation of the arc can be followed from Fig.7.1.

When the capacitance C and inductance L are connected across the arc, a current flows to charge the capacitor. As a result, less current flows in the arc and the voltage across it increases, until C is fully charged. At that point, the capacitor current falls, causing an increase in the arc current. The voltage across the arc then falls, causing the capacitor to discharge. The capacitor then recharges and the process is repeated at a rate determined by the circuit parameters.

The resistors R limited the arc current, and the heavy chokes I confined the oscillatory current to the loop formed by C, L and the arc. The chokes were located so that their

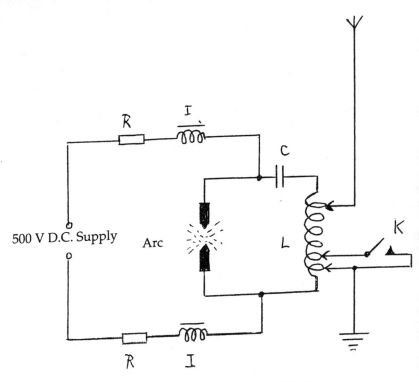

Fig.7.1 – Poulsen Arc Transmitter (1918)

strong magnetic field traversed the gas-tight chamber in which the electrodes were contained. The magnetic field stabilised the arc and a gentle flow of gas, such as hydrogen or coal gas, in the chamber, cooled the arc and improved its performance. The absence of air also extended the life of the electrodes. Because of the large amount of energy generated, the electrodes were of a substantial size, being made of copper (anode + ve) and carbon (cathode - ve). Cooling water circulated through the hollow interior of the copper anode, and the chamber itself was also water cooled. In spite of various steps taken to extend the life of the electrodes, the carbons had to be renewed frequently and the copper electrodes every two or three months.

The aerial and earth were connected directly on to the tuning coil L, but the manner in which the transmitter was keyed proved unusual. The arc had to remain energised continuously, and could not itself be keyed directly. In practice, with the contact K open, the transmitter radiated at a certain frequency f_1. When keyed, contact K short circuited a turn or two in the coil L, thereby changing the frequency of the transmitter to a frequency f_2, not far removed from f_1, and the receiver was sharply tuned to f_2; the energy radiated at f_1 was just wasted.

6.8 The Alexanderson Alternator

The Alexanderson alternator was a rotary generator, giving an output of up to 200kW, at frequencies as high as 100kHz. It was a type of machine now known as a variable-reluctance generator.

The frequency of an alternator can be increased, by increasing the speed of rotation of the shaft, by increasing the number of pairs of poles, or by increasing both. However, serious problems may arise when the frequency is extended into the radio-frequency band. At the required speed of rotation, a wound rotor could be torn apart by centrifugal forces, and the lubrication of the rotor bearings could also prove difficult. Advantages are to be gained by eliminating brushes and their associated commutators or slip rings, and excessive high-frequency losses have to be avoided in the overall design of the machine, especially in the magnetic material.

The essential principles of a variable-reluctance generator are shown in Fig.8.1, where a portion of the stator and rotor has been shown in a linear diagrammatic form. Each pole on the stator is wound with two separate coils. One, the field coil, carries a high direct current, to produce a strong

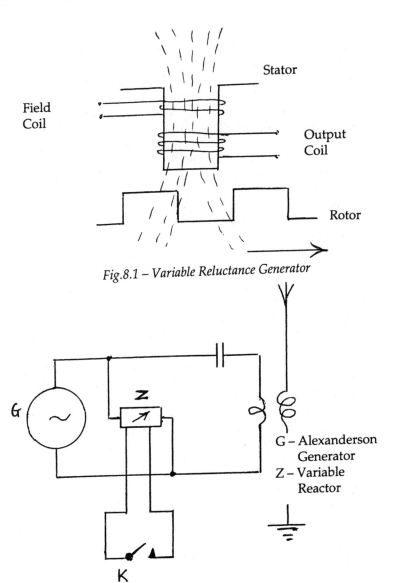

Fig.8.1 – Variable Reluctance Generator

Fig.8.2 – Alexanderson Transmitter (1920)

magnetic field throughout the machine. The second coil produces the output of the machine, all the coils, on the separate pole pieces, being connected in series aiding. When a tooth in the rotor is positioned opposite a stator pole, the magnetic flux cutting the output coil is at a maximum value, but when a slot in the rotor is opposite a pole, the flux in the coil is at a minimum. As the rotor spins around at high speed, the flux cutting the output coils fluctuates rapidly between a maximum and minimum value, and an alternating voltage is generated in the output coils.

The very large machines installed at Waunfawr were rated at 200kW, with outputs of about 21 and 31kHz respectively, and their rotor speeds would be between about 2000 and 3000 revolutions per minute. The drive was provided by an electric motor, through a suitable gear train. To reduce wind resistance, the slots in the rotor were filled with a non-magnetic metal, and the rotor was then carefully machined to give a smooth surface.

Sharply-tuned aerials were used with the Alexanderson alternator, and receiver selectivity was also improving. In order to maintain a high degree of frequency stability from these machines, a servo system was introduced, which regulated the speed of the driving motor.

A simple circuit of a transmitter, based on the Alexanderson alternator, is shown in Fig.8.2 The remote-keying relay contact K controls a variable reactor Z. With the key at rest, the low impedance presented by Z effectively shunts the alternator output. When the key is operated, the reactor changes to a high impedance and the alternator output is applied to the aerial.

6.9 The Valve Transmitter

By 1914, thermionic valves were available for low-power use in electronic circuits but because of major design and

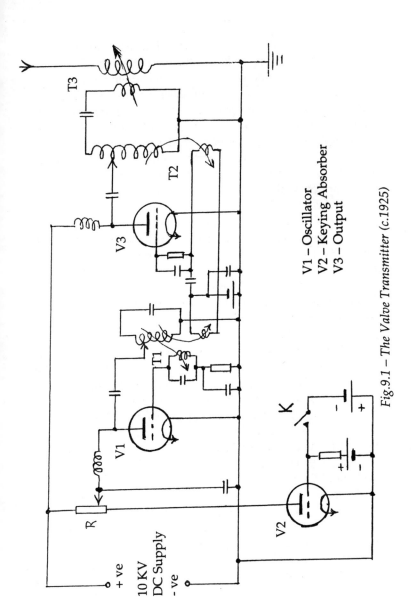

V1 – Oscillator
V2 – Keying Absorber
V3 – Output

Fig.9.1 – The Valve Transmitter (c.1925)

manufacturing problems, large transmitting valves, with power capacities of many kilowatts, were not available until a few years later. A powerful transmitter, rated at 100kW or more, would have a number of these valves in its output stage, all connected in parallel, so as to share the load between them. Anode voltages of 10-15kV were commonplace, derived either from the public mains supply or from a number of direct-current generators, each rated at about 5kV, connected in series. The filament of each valve was supplied with a heating current of 30-50 amperes, at a voltage of 20-40 volts.

Some of the power supplied to a valve appeared as heat in the anode which, under certain conditions, could glow red hot. In the case of valves with moderate output power, the glass envelope was cooled by a blast of air, but valves of greater power required a more effective means of cooling. By about 1920, a technique had been perfected of sealing glass on to copper, and this made possible the manufacture of large valves in which a copper anode formed an external extension of the glass envelope. In use, the anode was enclosed in an insulated jacket, which enabled a cooling liquid, usually water, to circulate around it. Where the local water supply was not suitable, distilled water was used in a closed loop, that included a heat exchanger. This was itself cooled by a flow of cold water from a local source, such as a lake or river. Pure water is a good insulator and the pipes to the valve jackets were of reliable insulating material, to withstand the high anode voltage.

In those early years, each transmitter was assembled on site, as a testbed, and modifications were frequently carried out, in the light of test results. A simple circuit diagram of a typical long-wave, high-power, wireless-telegraph transmitter, from about 1925, is shown in Fig.9.1. This operated in the continuous-wave (cw) mode, transmitting signals of constant amplitude, which could only be detected by a receiver fitted with a heterodyne oscillator. In Fig.9.1, a single valve symbol may represent a stage where a number of valves were connected in parallel, so as to carry the load. The oscillator valve V1 is switched ON and OFF by the current flow in the absorber valve V2. When the remote-keying relay contact K is open, a positive bias on the grid of V2 allows it to conduct, and the voltage drop across R reduces the anode voltage on V1, thus inhibiting its operation. V2 is designed to carry a high grid current for long periods, without damage.

When K is closed, an appropriate negative bias is applied to the grid of V2, which turns it off. With no V2 current flowing in R, the V1 anode voltage increases, and a transmitter signal is produced. This is amplified in the power stage V3, and an output passes on to the aerial. Coupling coils T1, T2 and T3 are all tuned to the transmitter frequency. An inductive coupling from T2 feeds a carefully balanced amount of energy back from the output to the grids of V1 and V3, thereby increasing the output power.

Before the introduction of thermionic valves, the remote keying of a high-power wireless transmitter relied on the use of specialised high-voltage relays. These responded to incoming line signals, of about 20 milliamperes, which had originated from a Morse key or Wheatstone transmitter at the controlling station. At the transmitter, the line signals operated a Creed telegraph relay, at speeds of up to 100 words per minute or more, and the relay armature activated an ingenious arrangement of levers, slide valves and pistons. The slide valves directed the flow of compressed air to operate two pistons in sequence, and the second piston in the chain caused the high-voltage contacts to make or break. The contact assembly had to withstand a voltage of several kilovolts and was mounted on large, hollow, insulating pillars. Although the contacts were made and broken very rapidly by the force of the compressed air, it was found necessary to direct a blast of air, from a blower, up the hollow insulating pillars, so as to quench any arcing at the contacts.

In the earliest high-power valve transmitters, a resistor was included in the anode circuit of the oscillator valve, which inhibited its operation. When the high-voltage relay contacts closed, this resistor was short-circuited, allowing the oscillator stage to be energised. Before long, this arrangement was replaced by one in which the keying was effected at a valve grid, as shown in Fig.9.1. This was a point of relatively low voltage and of low current. Much simpler keying relays were suitable with this new technique and the high-voltage relays became obsolete.

Bibliography

The books listed below were consulted in the preparation of this account.

Baker, E.C., *Sir William Preece FRS, Victorian Engineer Extraordinary*, Hutchinson & Co., 1976

Vyvyan, R.N., *Wireless over Thirty Years*, George Routledge & Sons Ltd., 1933

Baker, W.J., *A History of the Marconi Company*, Methuen & Co.Ltd., 1970

Jolly, W.P., *Marconi – A Biography*, Constable & Co.Ltd., 1972

Stanley, R., *Text-Book on Wireless Telegraphy, Volume I*, Longmans, Green & Co., 1919

Dowsett, H.M., *Wireless Telegraphy and Telephony*, The Wireless Press Ltd., 1920

Acknowledgements

1. Information supplied by the individuals and organisations listed below has proved invaluable and is much appreciated:

N. Johannessen, BT Museum, London; I.J. Forster, GEC – Marconi Research Centre, Chelmsford; R. Rodwell and Miss L. Weymouth, GEC – Marconi Archives, Chelmsford; B.T. Archives, London; Public Records Offices, Caernarfon and Dolgellau; D. Roberts, Chairman, Dragon Amateur Radio Club; M. Rickard, Local Historian, Tywyn; Mr & Mrs Rees, Escuan Hall, Tywyn; Mr & Mrs Wynstanley, Penrhos, Caeathro; Mrs Eunice Williams, Bryn Helen, Caernarfon.

2. Photographs are included courtesy of the sources listed below, and these are shown adjacent to each plate:

David Williams
GEC – Marconi Ltd.
IEE Archives
'Electronics World', formerly 'The Wireless World'.
'Caernarfon and Denbigh Herald' (The Herald), photo: Arwyn Roberts
Mrs Eunice Williams

3. The author wishes to thank the publishers who currently hold the copyright on the books referred to below, for their permission to include certain line diagrams in this account. These diagrams are based loosely on similar drawings in these books:

Fig.1.3 to Fig.5.1 – *A History of the Marconi Company* by W.J. Baker, 1970. Courtesy Methuen & Co.
Fig.6.1 – *Wireless Telegraphy and Telephony*, by H.M. Dowsett, 1920. Courtesy 'Electronics World'.
Fig.7.1 – *Text-Book on Wireless Telegraphy Vol.I*, by R. Stanley, 1919. Courtesy Addison, Wesley, Longman Ltd.
Fig.9.1 – A paper entitled *Cooled – Anode Valves and Lives of*

Transmitting Valves, by W.J. Picken. Published in *The Journal of the Institution of Electrical Engineers*, Volume 65, in 1927. Courtesy the IEE.

Illustrations

The illustrations are credited as follows:

William Henry Preece – IEE Archives
Bryn Helen – Mrs Eunice Williams
Penrhos, Caeathro and two memorial plaques
– David Williams
Pioneer operators at Tywyn – Electronics World
Report of Princess Elettra's visit – Photo by Arwyn Roberts
All other photographs – GEC – Marconi Ltd.

Index